More Tuppenny Laffs with Finbarr Saunders and his Double Entendres

FINBARR—IT'S TIME FOR YOUR DRIVING LESSON. MR GIMLET SAYS HE'LL TAKE YOU OUT AND GIVE YOU A QUICK ONE IN HIS CAR.

ARF! ARF!

FNUK! FNUK!

HOO! HOO!

SOON— ALWAYS CHECK OVER YOUR CAR BEFORE SETTING OFF. VISIBILITY IS MOST IMPORTANT. YOUR MOTHER LIKES ME TO GIVE HER HEADLAMPS A GOOD RUB AT LEAST ONCE A WEEK.

HO! HO!

INSPECT EACH TYRE FOR SIGNS OF WEAR OR LOW PRESSURE. REMEMBER, THE HARDER IT IS, THE MORE COMFORTABLE YOUR RIDE WILL BE.

FWOOOAAR! FWOOOAAR!

KWOOO! KWOOO!

YAK! YAK!

TRY TO KEEP YOUR VEHICLE UNDER COVER IN BAD WEATHER. THE FLAPS WILL GET WET AND MESSY, SO GIVE THEM A WIPE AFTER YOU TAKE IT OUT.

HAAAR! HAAAR!

AK! AK! AK!

I LOVE THE SUMMER. MY CAR HAS A SOFT TOP, AND THERE'S NOTHING I LIKE MORE THAN HAVING IT OFF ON A SUNNY DAY.

K-SNUK! K-SNUK!

YOOO! YOOO!

RIGHT— LET'S START THE ENGINE. THAT'S THE CHOKE. GRASP THE KNOB FIRMLY AND PULL IT OUT.

COOAARP! COOAARP!

HO! HO!

ONCE YOU'VE GOT HER WARMED UP YOU CAN PUSH IT ALL THE WAY IN.

F-SNUUUUR! F-SNUUUUR!

HAAA! HAAA!

YIK! YIK!

OKAY— OFF WE GO. BE CAREFUL NOT TO PULL OFF TOO QUICKLY OR YOU MIGHT HAVE AN ACCIDENT.

YURP! YURP!

ARF! ARF!

NOOK! NOOK!

LOTS OF PEOPLE ASK ME FOR LIFTS, AND I WAS ONCE GIVING YOUR MOTHER ONE WHEN I PULLED OUT TOO EARLY.

FNURR! FNURR!

KWOO! KWOO!

HO! HO! HO!

THERE WAS A BIG BANG AND AN AWFUL MESS.

I'VE BEEN DRIVING FOR YEARS. BEFORE THAT I USED TO RIDE A MOTORBIKE. THE FIRST TIME I DID IT WAS IN A FIELD WHEN I WAS 14.

I SCRATCHED MY HELMET ON A THISTLE.

S-WOOF! S-WOOF!

AG! AG!

IT WAS A BUMPY NARROW TRACK AND I CAME OFF AFTER TWO OR THREE BOUNCES.

STEERING IS A DIFFICULT BUSINESS. THE FASTER YOU GO, THE HARDER IT GETS.

KARK! KARK!

YIG! YIG!

TRY TO KEEP YOUR HANDS TIGHTLY ON THE RIM.

NOW, FINBARR— SEE IF YOU CAN SLIP IT THROUGH THIS NARROW GAP.

B-SNURK! B-SNURK!

WOOOAGH! WOOOAGH!

GWOOOOAAR!

MODERN SMALL CARS ARE EASY TO MANOEUVRE. I USED TO HAVE A LONG ONE...

HARF! HARF!

FNODOP! FNODOP!

AND I REMEMBER— I ONCE GOT IT STUCK BETWEEN A PAIR OF BRISTOLS.

PEOPLE ARE ALWAYS BUYING ME ACCESSORIES. THESE SEAT COVERS WERE A GIFT FROM MY WIFE...

HMMP! HMMP!

WHILST YOUR MOTHER GAVE ME THE HORN THE OTHER MORNING AFTER BREAKFAST.

GO ON FINBARR— GIVE THE END A SQUEEZE! YOUR MOTHER LIKES TO BLOW IT WHEN NO-ONE IS LOOKING.

FNARR! FNARR!

OH DEAR. I THINK WE'VE BROKEN DOWN. MY WIFE HAS SOME SPARES FOR THIS CAR...

HOO! HOO!

HOO! HOO!

HOO! HOO!

BUT THESE DAYS I DON'T OFTEN HAVE THE CHANCE TO GET MY HANDS ON HER PARTS.

THERE'S A COLLAPSIBLE RED WARNING TRIANGLE IN THE BOOT. GET IT OUT, ERECT IT, AND SHOW IT TO PASSING MOTORISTS.

GWOO!

G-WOOOOO!

I'M GOING TO NEED HELP. I'LL WALK BACK TO YOUR MOTHER'S HOUSE AND SEE IF I CAN GET A BIT.

HI! HI!

AG! AG! AG!

K-WURK! K-WURK!

SEVERAL HOURS LATER—

OOOH MR GIMLET! THAT'S A BIG END.

YES MRS SAUNDERS. AND JUST LOOK AT THE LENGTH OF THE SHAFT!

MUM AND MR GIMLET MUST BE LOOKING AT A DIAGRAM OF THE CAR IN THE WORKSHOP MANUAL.

THE FISH SUPPER

Prime fillet of issues 43 to 47 in a crispy batter coating. With chips.

Written, drawn and produced by
Chris Donald (Editor)
Graham Dury   Simon Thorp
Simon Donald

With contributions from
Davey Jones   John Fardell
and Gary Robinson

Photography by Colin Davison

ISBN 1-870870-28-X

Published in Great Britain by John Brown Publishing Limited,
The Boathouse, Crabtree Lane, Fulham, London SW6 8NJ.

First (and probably last) printing, September 1992, or thereabouts

Printed and bound in Great Britain

LeTTeRBox

LETTERBOCKS,
VIZ COMIC
P.O. BOX 1PT
NEWCASTLE UPON TYNE
NE99 1PT

Let's forgive and forget

Why are people kicking up such a fuss about the re-unification of Germany. Isn't it about time we forgot the past? Just because these people have already started two world wars, after promising they wouldn't, isn't any reason for us to mistrust them.
N. Roper
Oldham

Like most of the British public I am outraged by sex and violence on TV, but unlike the 'moaning minnies' I simply turn off my TV when offensive programmes appear. Likewise, when I purchase my copy of Viz every two months, I simply refuse to read it.
R. Sayle
Corbridge

Let's have a picture of a train

How about a picture of a train? The lads in the army over here miss them terribly as there are no trains in Cyprus. A picture would certainly brighten our day.
Stuart Whitlan
17/21 Lancers, Cyprus

● *Here you are Stuart, here's a train especially for all the members of the armed forces serving in Cyprus.*
Are you serving overseas in the army, navy or air force and miss the everyday sights of home? Perhaps you're a soldier in Belize who'd like to see a London bus, or a sailor who's at sea and yearns for the sight of a telephone kiosk. Why not write and let us know.

Driving home the other day I was unable to get a decent reception on my car radio so I decided to whistle my favourite tune instead. Imagine my disappointment when I arrived home before it had finished.
Granville Canty
Hebden Bridge

Letts Diaries

I arrived at work the other day to find that the place had been reduced to a pile of rubble. I had to laugh when my boss reminded me – I'm a demolition engineer.
B. Liar
Essex

Napoleon once described Britain as 'a nation of shop-keepers'. That's nonsense. My father is a plumber, and has been for 48 years.
Duncan Watson
Preston

The good old days

In the old days if we wanted to go out to a dance we had to wear my mother's bedroom curtains, and paint shoes on our feet using my grandad's army boot polish. And we had to be home by ten o'clock so that my mother could draw the curtains when she went to bed. I couldn't believe my ears last week when my grandson, who is two, asked for £600 to buy a pair of these modern 'training shoes' to wear in the pub. Has the world gone mad?
Mrs Ada Brady
Golden Pastures Rest Home
Fulchester

I pity today's youngsters trying to make a living for themselves. Schools are run down and under-staffed, and old industries are dying, with unemployment rife. For many there is no job, and no future.
If my wife and I have children we intend to drown them in a bucket of water, and would recommend other readers in depressed areas do likewise.
T. McMahon
Liverpool

The Black and White Minstrel Show

Experts fear that beef being eaten today may cause 'mad cow' symptoms to develop in our children in 10 or 20 years time. I therefore refuse to allow my children to eat any beef whatsoever. Instead I give it to my mother who is 87 and will be dead in a year or two anyway.
Irene Saddleworth
Buckstead

If Sinead O'Connor grew her hair a bit and bought herself a nice frock she'd make a lovely wife for some lucky young man.
Mrs. E. Roach
Durham

Rising mortgage rates don't bother me at all. I'm a Brazilian and consequently I don't have to pay back any money which I borrow from the bank.
Jesus Carambos Iguana
Cricklewood

Sunday Night at the London Palladium

I am busy restoring an old 1960's Ever Ready torch, and am looking for spares. Do any of your readers have two U2 batteries and a small bulb?
R. Paul
Gibraltar

A friend once told me the most dangerous part of a car is 'the nut behind the steering wheel'. Following his advice I romoved this nut from my car. Later, whilst travelling at speed on a dual carriageway, the steering wheel became detached, and the car spun across the central reservation and collided head-on with an oncoming lorry. It just goes to show, you shouldn't believe everything people tell you.
T. Rodgers
Arbroath

TopTips

WHEN holidaying abroad include a toilet brush and a standard lamp in your luggage. Hotels rarely provide toilet brushes, and the lamp will come in very handy for reading.
Mrs. D. Patterson
Shrewsbury

PRETEND you're German when on holiday by being rude to other holiday-makers, over-eating and barging into queues.
T. Pearson
Hull

DON'T waste money buying 'Big Country's Greatest Hits' album. Simply buy one of their 7″ singles and play it over and over again.
Paul Goss
Basildon

STICK a dead goldfish inside the cover of library books. The smell of the fish will act as a reminder that the book is overdue for return.
Doris Franklin
Weymouth

MAKE visits to the dentist less nerve racking by dropping into the pub first and drinking 5 or 6 pints of beer.
T. Horswill
Bedford

It's happening, It's great And it's here on page 6

6

PRINCE'S DRAMATIC ADMISSION

EXCLUSIVE

HRH Prince Edward yesterday issued a shock statement which put an end to months of public speculation. "Yes", he declared, "I AM theatrical".

A close friend told us that the Prince has been aware of his theatrical tendencies since early schooldays. "Edward used to dress slightly flamboyantly and talk in a loud voice. By the age of 13 he was gesticulating two or three times a day".

ASHAMED

It was during his time at Cambridge Edward began to realise that being theatrical was nothing to be ashamed of. He began to mix with and feel comfortable in the company of other theatricals.

TENDENCIES

However, under constant pressure from his family, the Prince tried to disguise his tendencies by playing competitive sports, talking in a stern voice and joining the army. But all along, deep down inside, he knew he was a theatrical, and it was probably in 1986 that he made his decision to leave the Marines and live openly as a theatrical person. His parents were shocked and disappointed but Edward knew he had made the right decision.

BENT

Doctors believe that up to 1 in 10 people in Britain have a theatrical bent, although many try to lead normal lives, disguising their true feelings from family and friends. But nowadays being thespian no longer has the same social stigma attached

to it that it did in Oscar Wilde's day. That is the view of Dr. Quentin Bender, social psychologist at the Brighton Institute of Dramatic Art and Interior Design. And Hairdressing.

UPHILL GARDENER

"If people feel they are harbouring dramatic tendencies they should contact their local amateur dramatic society for help and counselling", he told us. Other well-known theatricals have included Danny La Rue, Larry Grayson and Noël Coward.

Celebrity Swears

Nº 207

David Coleman

HAIRY ARSEHOLES

MAKE cactus plants safe for young children by removing all the spines with a pair of tweezers.
Gillian Tasker
Derbyshire

BRIGHTEN UP dull Monday mornings at work by concealing a bottle of vodka in your jacket pocket and taking swigs from it at regular intervals throughout the day.
T. Horswill
Bedford

DON'T spend a fortune buying expensive oven gloves. Boxing gloves, available from most sports shops, will do the job just as well.
M. Cartwright
Borth

ENSURE a good night's sleep by knocking back a large bottle of gin before retiring to bed.
T. Horswill
Bedford

BISCUIT WISE
by little Ern

Drop your biscuit queries to Little Ern, Biscuit Wise, P.O. Box 1PT, Newcastle upon Tyne NE99 1PT. We regret that all letters will be thrown away unopened.

Chocolate Hob-Nob problem

Dear Little Ern,
I particularly enjoy the new 'Hob Nob' biscuits, especially the chocolate coated variety. However, my husband enjoys milk chocolate, while I prefer plain.
Do you know of any plans afoot to introduce a packet containing both?
Mrs Rosemary Nutmeg Parsley, Herts.

● *Sorry Rosemary, but my friends at McVities tell me that mixing their delicious milk and plain chocolate Hob Nobs would be technically impossible.*
Ern's Biscuit Tip: *Why not buy one packet of each, and mix them yourself in a small tin or similar air tight container. Special 'biscuit barrels' are available from many stores, starting from around £2.00.*

Dear Little Ern,
My hubby insists on calling Cream Crackers 'biscuits', but I was always told that these were 'savoury wafers' as they do not contain sugar and can be eaten with cheese. Who is right?
Basil Bayleaf Dill, Cheshire

● *Oh no! Not the old 'biscuit/ wafer' debate again. If I had a Custard Cream for everytime this one has cropped up, I'd have an awful lot of biscuits! Let's call a truce – both of you are right. Cream Crackers are, technically speaking, wafers, as they contain more salt than sugar. However the cheese rule does not always apply, as we've all ate Digestives with cheese, haven't we. And who hasn't enjoyed wafers with ice cream. Tricky, isn't it. Anyway, biscuit or wafer, whatever you call them, they all taste lovely.*

Dear Little Ern,
As a child I vividly remember my grandmother giving me flat, crunchy, glazed shortcake biscuits with a thin layer of crushed raisins inside. For the life of me I cannot remember what they were called. Do these biscuits still exist, and if so, where can I get a packet?
Mrs Corriander Sage Thyme, Middlesex

● *The biscuits you describe sound to me like Garibaldi, a particular favourite of mine too. Traditional Scottish biscuit manufacturers Crawfords still manufacture Garibaldi in their 'Pennywise' range, priced from around 25p for a 300 gram packet.*

Dear Little Ern,
I've been eating Coconut Creams since I was five, and I'm convinced that today's biscuits contain less coconut than they used to. Are the manufacturers penny pinching here?
Mrs Mint Marjoram Cumin, Mid Glamorgan

● *Well Mrs Marjoram, on reading your letter I popped out to my local biscuit supplier and nibbled a couple of Coconut Creams on my way home. And they seemed alright to me. Of course not all manufacturers maintain the same high standards, and a lot depends on the brand of biscuit you're eating. Why not treat yourself to a Fox's Family Assortment. You'll find some first rate Coconut Creams in there, not to mention a few other biscuit delights!*

Biscuit of the Week

This week I've selected Peak Freans 'Bourbons' as my biscuit of the week. With their fondant chocolate centre sandwiched between rich, sugar coated biscuit fingers, it's no wonder they say 'You can't beat a Bourbon'. I'm off to enjoy a packet now out on the patio with a nice pot of tea. See you next week. And in the meantime, keep crunching!

LET'S FACE IT. THINGS JUST AREN'T WORKING OUT BETWEEN US.

Billy the Fish

Fulchester United have been rocked by manager Tommy Brown's shock revelation that he is a woman, Samantha, pregnant with Billy "The Fish" Thomson's love child...

NOW READ ON...

THE NEXT DAY, THE MANAGERESS IS LATE FOR TRAINING...

I WONDER WHERE SAMANTHA IS.

YES, SHE'S BRINGING A CAKE RECIPE FOR MY WIFE TODAY.

SUDDENLY, A STRANGER APPEARS...

HELLO...

WHO'S THIS?

YOU DON'T KNOW ME, BUT SAMANTHA BROWN ASKED ME TO DELIVER A MESSAGE.

SHE HAS GONE TO BRAZIL FOR EVER. I AM HER TWIN BROTHER THOMAS, AND I WILL BE TAKING OVER AS MANAGER OF FULCHESTER UNITED.

FAIR ENOUGH. YOU'RE THE BOSS NOW, THOMAS.

JUST CALL ME TOMMY, SYD.

GATHER ROUND LADS. WE'VE GOT A TOUGH GAME ON SATURDAY, AGAINST ROSSDALE ROVERS.

BUT ROSSDALE HAVEN'T WON A MATCH IN EIGHT YEARS!

YES, THEY'RE BOTTOM OF THE LEAGUE AREN'T THEY?

YES, BUT THEY'VE JUST SIGNED STUMPY ARGENTINIAN CHEAT DIEGO MARADONA FOR 10 MILLION POUNDS. HE COULD PROVE QUITE A HANDFUL ON SATURDAY.

WE'VE GOT TO KEEP IT TIGHT AT THE BACK, PICK UP THE SPARE MAN, USE THE WIDTH OF THE PARK AND LET THE BALL DO THE WORK.

GOOD THINKING BOSS.

HOPEFULLY, AT THE END OF THE NINETY MINUTES WE'LL COME AWAY WITH SOME SORT OF RESULT.

SATURDAY ARRIVES - AND A CAPACITY CROWD CRAMS INTO FULCHESTER STADIUM TO WATCH THE FOUR FOOT ARGENTINIAN ACE'S DEBUT FOR ROSSDALE...

MARADONA KICKS OFF FOR ROSSDALE...

PHEEP!

HANDBALL! SURELY!

THE REFEREE MUST BE BLIND!

FREE KICK TO ROSSDALE!

PHEEP!

THE REF'S SHOWING ONE OF THE UNITED PLAYERS THE YELLOW CARD!

CRUMBS!

BUT REF! I NEVER TOUCHED HIM!

A POTENTIALLY DANGEROUS SITUATION EH, BOSS?

YES SYD.

THE ROSSDALE FORWARDS COULD PRODUCE SOMETHING FROM THERE, BILLY THE FISH COULD BE CALLED UPON TO PROVE HIS WORTH!

THE FREE KICK IS TAKEN...

S GO! DISCS GO!

IT'S A CURLING, DIPPING CROSS, AIMED AT THE FAR POST.

YES, BUT AT FOUR FOOT TWO, MARADONA WON'T BE ABLE TO GET ANYWHERE NEAR IT.

BILLY'S GOT THAT ONE SAFELY COVERED.

BUT—

BUT NO! BILLY'S BEEN BEATEN!

LOB

GOAL TO ROSSDALE!

?

SHADES OF HANDBALL, EH BOSS?

IT CERTAINLY LOOKED THAT WAY FROM WHERE I'M SITTING, BUT THE REFEREE WAS WELL POSITIONED TO JUDGE FOR HIMSELF... AND HIS DECISION IS FINAL.

FULCHESTER REPLY WITH A QUICK BREAK...

BROWN FOX HAS A CLEAR RUN AT THE ROSSDALE GOAL!

YES!

UM FOUL!

FREE KICK SURELY!

TRIP!

LOONY LEFTIES SET TO KILL EVERYONE!

We have uncovered a sinister plot to **ASSASSINATE** hundreds of top politicians, show business celebrities and members of the Royal Family.

Drug crazed animal rights extremists plan to wipe out **EVERYONE** who eats meat, and that includes things like sausages, cornish pasties and even tinned ravioli. And police fear that the lunatics' hit list could include several **MILLION** names. Among them the Queen, Margaret Thatcher, and top news reader Sir Alistair Burnett.

DEATH LIST

Top of the death list would be blood sports enthusiasts and food barons like turkey king Bernard Matthews, Captain Birds Eye and Mr. Kipling.

EXTREMISTS

Posing as drop-out, drug-crazed, left-wing layabout extremists, our reporters managed to infiltrate the seedy south London squat which acts as headquarters for a group of smelly, long-haired, unwashed hippies who are master-minding the murderous plot.

ARSENAL

We were greeted at the door of the squalid basement flat by Malcolm Evans, an odourous, flea-ridden, communist subversive drug addict who boasted of his plans to terrorise Britain.

Long haired vegetarian hippies plan terror blitz on Britain

Underneath a urine-soaked mattress in a damp rat-infested back bedroom we were shown a terrifying arsenal which Evans and his festering, filth-ridden, greasy cohorts had amassed in readiness for their planned terror blitz.

CHELSEA

This included a bread knife, a garden fork, a catapult, several marbles and a sinister empty Smash tin. "That's going to be a bomb", he told us. "We are going to get some explosives to put inside it. And a battery".

CRYSTAL PALACE

Top of the lazy, layabout good-for-nothing hippies' death list is TV astrologer Patrick Moore, who, according to Evans, eats ham and mushroom quiche. We were

Some animals yesterday.

shown a black book containing the names of dozens of well-known celebrities, among them Esther Rantzen, football commentator Brian Moore and weather girl Trish Williams.

SPURS

According to Evans, Rantzen eats sausages, Moore has gone fishing in the past and Williams likes tomato soup.

STIRRUPS

New Scotland Yard anti-terrorist chiefs are already aware of Evans' activities. An earlier terror campaign ended in his arrest after he was punched in the face outside a pie shop in Wimbledon. He was later fined £25 for behaviour likely to cause a breach of the peace.

MOORE

MATTHEWS

BIRDSEYE

WE INJECT QUEEN WITH ORANGE JUICE

Police are thought to be taking seriously threats by a former Twycross Zoo employee who claims that he will inject the Queen with 'monkey chemicals' if £150 is not paid into his Post Office savings account by mid-day tomorrow.

In a note sent to Buckingham Palace, former zoo auxilliary Trevor Balderstone says that unless the cash is paid on time, the Queen will be injected with the rare monkey chemicals stolen from the zoo. And as a result she will become hairy, eat bananas and live in a tree.

Zoo man's ape threat to Queen

"I'm not joking", says Balderstone, 27, an out-patient at a Leicestershire mental hospital. "I've got the chemicals and I mean business".

A spokesman for Twycross Zoo admitted that a small quantity of monkey chemicals was missing, but added that is was probably not enough to cause a permanent monkey transformation in the Queen.

PEANUTS

"She'll probably just eat a few peanuts and scratch herself under the arms a bit. And perhaps her arse will go blue for a day or so".

Is this the future face of the Queen? (above)

Our reporter managed to penetrate royal security as the Queen went on a walkabout in Milton Keynes town centre yesterday. Despite a high profile police presence, our man was able to inject the Queen with half a pint of harmless orange juice. "It could just as easily have been monkey chemicals", he told us afterwards.

TOPLESS
Skateboard Nun

One day, Sister Mary and her Mother Superior were taking a quiet stroll in the country.

WHAT A BEAUTIFUL DAY IT IS, SISTER MARY.

Suddenly...

QUICK, THE DAM. IT'S CRACKING.

The two nuns went to investigate.

OH NO! THE SCHOOL BUS. IT'S BROKEN DOWN ON THE DAM. ALL THOSE CHILDREN ARE IN DANGER.

IF ONLY WE COULD HELP. ALL WE CAN DO IS PRAY FOR THEM.

But Sister Mary knew exactly what she must do...

And in seconds, she had transformed herself into...

...Topless Skateboard Nun!

In a flash she had skated across the crumbling dam to the stricken bus...

COR, JESUS!

QUICK. THERE'S NO TIME TO EXPLAIN. FOLLOW ME.

A TEAM

The children were soon being led to safety.

MICHAEL ROW THE BOAT ASHORE HALLELOOOOOO YAH

A few hours later, the dam gave way.

Shortly...

THANK YOU, TOPLESS SKATEBOARD NUN, WHOEVER YOU ARE. YOU SAVED THOSE CHILDREN'S LIVES.

BLESS YOU, MY SON.

WA-HAY. DOWN BOY.

NEXT WEEK – Nymphomaniac Pogo-Stick Nurse.

HOUSE OF HO

Britain's MPs are the ugliest in the world — and that's official.

And since live TV cameras were turned on in the Commons, the British public has been **TURNED OFF** by the sight of their Right 'Horrible' Members' faces.

A report published this week **SLAMS** Britain's unsightly politicians, claiming that most of them are:

● **FAT**

● **BALDING**

● or have some other **UN-PLEASANT** physical characteristic.

UGLY

And it **NAMES** many 'ugly' MPs, accusing:
● **MRS THATCHER** of being 'old, wrinkly' and having a 'baggy throat'
● **NEIL KINNOCK** of being 'pointy nosed'

PHOTOGRAPHS

The twelve page report is the result of an independent study by Professor Oswald Cinamon-Chives, senior political analyst at Grimsby College of Further Education. He spent several months looking at photographs of MPs, and he believes his report spells out a clear warning to party leaders on all sides of the political spectrum.

VOTES

"Unless attractive MPs can be found, and quickly, **MILLIONS** of votes will be lost in the next election."

Professor Cinamon-Chives

Professor Cinamon-Chives has sent copies of his report to the leaders of all Britain's major political parties, naming the politicians who he feels are the least attractive. But so far there has been no response from party spokesmen.

AWARE

In recent months, however, there have been signs that politicians are becoming more aware of the importance of looking good. Some action is being taken to improve the public image of leading MPs, with professional public relations consultants giving advice. But Professor Cinamon-Chives fears that it could be a case of too little, too late.

Thatcher – 'baggy throat'

Kinnock – 'pointy nose'

"You can't make a silk purse out of a sow's ear," he told us. "And no amount of elocution, grooming, make-up and clever lighting will hide a large nose or a big, wobbly double chin.

SEX

Professor Cinamon-Chives believes that a staggering 95% of Britain's 630 MPs are so unattractive that their constituents simply wouldn't want to have sex with them if the opportunity arose. "If you're not prepared to go to bed with someone, then why on earth should you vote for them?" asked the professor.

NEIGHBOURS

Professor Cinamon-Chives believes that Britain is lagging behind our European neighbours, many of whom have attractive politicians.

HOME & AWAY

"Take Czechoslovakia for example. Their president is very good looking. You don't see ugly Italian MPs, and even the French president isn't that bad looking, from certain angles."

SKIPPY

In 1992 Professor Cinamon-Chives fears that Britain will pay the price for its ugly politicians. "Relaxed border controls will mean that people can vote for whoever they want, and if the candidates are better looking in France, Italy or Spain, then they will get the votes. By the year 2000 we could see a British parliament made up entirely of foreign MPs."

Lawson – 'fat old woman'

Britten – 'lumpy face'

Channon – 'funny eyes'

Major – 'silver hair'

IT'S GOING UP AGAIN

Only months after celebrating the removal of the Berlin Wall, East and West German officials have decided to **RE-BUILD** it!

This dramatic turn around is a result of parking problems in Berlin city centre. Motorists using the city's many parking meters are flooding into *East* Berlin to take advantage of cheaper parking rates.

And in *West* Berlin skint East Germans are being forced to park on double yellow lines rather than pay the extortionate rates charged by the West Germans.

HELVETICA

The rebuilding of the wall, which will be topped with extra barbed wire, should be completed by 1991. In the meantime East German officials have been warned that West German motorists attempting to park their cars in the East will be shot.

12

RORS!

Moynihan – 'debonnaire'

Gummer – 'manly jaw'

UGLY MINISTERS GET THE CHOP

Ugly appearances are thought to have cost several top politicians their jobs in recent Cabinet shuffles as Mrs Thatcher tries to boost her popularity by surrounding herself with handsome ministers.

• **OUT** went ugly Nigel Lawson, who according to the report looks 'like a fat old woman'.

• **OUT** went Leon Britten, with his 'lumpy, Humpty Dumpty shaped face'.

• and **OUT** went Paul Channon, whose eyes are described as 'too far apart, and pointing down in the middle'.

• **IN** came John Major, with his 'distinctive silver hair and manly voice'.

• **IN** came 'dashing, debonnaire' Colin Moynihan, former Olympic athlete and Commons heart-throb.

• and **IN** came charmer John Selwyn-Gummer, with his 'manly square jaw' and 'come-to-bed eyes'.

SPECTRUM

The report criticises MPs from all sides of the political spectrum. Labour's Roy Hattersley is singled out for having a 'fat, rubbery face with a dribbly bottom lip'.

MYSTERONS

Opposition colleague Robin Cook is described as having a 'light bulb shaped head' and 'frightening pixie-like features', while Clare Short comes under fire for having 'unpleasant

Hattersley – 'dribbly lip'

Cook – 'light bulb head'

teeth' and 'a face like a cow's arse'.

COLONEL WHITE

Former Social Democrat leader and one-time heart throb David Owen is accused of having 'women's tits', while former Liberal leader Sir David Steel is one of many MPs criticised for being 'too short'. He is also listed as having 'big ears' and a 'squeaky voice'.

CAPTAIN SCARLET

Only Liberal Democrat leader Paddy Ashdown comes away unscathed. Professor Cinamon-Chives describes the Yeovil MP and former marine as being a 'rugged, flame haired hunk of a man'.

Ashdown – 'rugged hunk'

Short – 'cow's arse'

13

ROGER MELLIE
The man on the telly

One morning in Tom's office... Roger, I've just had a call from 'After Darkness', Channel 4's open ended late night discussion programme. OH RIGHT! That's the one where everyone eats peanuts and gets pissed.

No Roger, that ISN'T the idea. Anyway, they've invited YOU to take part in tonight's programme. HEY, BRILLIANT! The subject under discussion will be 'Sexism in the media'. They want you to represent the views of the T.V. industry.

Sexism in the media eh? MMM... Tell me Tom... ...do they lay on all the booze, or would it be best if I take a few cans?

I believe refreshment is provided. But Roger, please GO EASY, eh? It's a live show, and it's a serious debate. Just stick to fruit juice, eh? TOM...

You know me. I'm a pro. I've been in this game long enough to know that booze and broadcasting don't mix! Mind you, perhaps I'd better take a couple of bottles along eh? Just to be polite.

Yes, well, whatever you do don't be late. They want you at the studio by eleven. No problem Tom. Leave it to me.

11.30 at the studio Well, we were expecting Roger Mellie to be joining us tonight, but there's no sign of him yet so we've had to start without him. First, let me introduce our other guests. No doubt Roger will be with us shortly. In the meantime, with me in the studio tonight are...

David O'Sullivan, publisher of the 'Sunday Spunk' and various other tabloid newspapers. Next to him Clare Shortarse, MP, 'Anti Page 3' campaigner.

Samantha Bucketfanny is best known for her work as a page 3 model... ...and has also appeared in several adult videos.

And finally Bobby Charlton, who's goals helped England to victory in the 1966 world cup.

Twenty minutes later... If you don't like my newspaper, you don't have to buy it... MUNCH! MUNCH!! Newspaper?! I wouldn't call it a newspaper!

Hey! Is this where the party is? I've brought a couple of mates with me. You don't mind do you? We've brought our own beer.

Oh my god! Quickly! Cut to the adverts! What the hell is going on?! ADVERTS ON OFF

For heaven's sake Roger. Who are these people? HERE WE GO! HERE WE GO! HERE WE GO! Hey! They're my best mates. They're alright they are. This is a T.V. studio, not a nightclub. Get them out of here!

Er... Tom invited us. Roger, sit down quickly! We're back on air now. Yeah... Nick said it would be okay. But I've left me coat through there. Shift your arse along a bit will you? Ta love.

Your 'newspapers' are pornographic rubbish Mr O'Sullivan, you exploit and degrade wimmin, and you are a fat slimey toad. So there. How do you answer that accusation David? I thought we were going to talk about SEX! Well Clare, if you don't like my newspaper, you don't have to buy it.

Really! You men are all alike. The issue here is SEXISM as opposed to sex. Yeah... HIC! Right. So how often do you get it, eh?

Not much by the look of it! She's got a face like a half sucked lemon. How typical. This is just the kind of overtly sexist media attitude that wimmin have to contend with every day.

Aah, come on love. You're not that bad. I was only kiddin', come on... let's all have another drink eh?

Samantha, we've been talking about exploitation of women by the media. As a topless model weren't you exploited? No, not at all. I'm not ashamed of my body. Page three is art, innit. Like all them old paintings n'that.

Page three. Of course! I knew I'd seen those before!

14

KING ARTHUR'S CASTLE

It looks like a Royal Palace, a home fit for a King. But believe it or not these **EXCLUSIVE** pictures reveal for the first time the multi-million pound luxury Barnsley home of miner's president Arthur Scargill.

Commie Scargill's palace bought with Nazi gold

This is the house that Arthur built.
● It has 280 bedrooms, two swimming pools, tennis courts and a private golf course.
● It houses a priceless art collection, over 1,000 paintings, sculptures and expensive vases.
● It is set in 800 acres of private woodlands, with a hunting lodge and prime salmon fishing.
● The servant's quarters alone are ten times as big as the average family home.
● It contains over 10 square miles of specially woven Persian carpet.
● It cost a staggering £100 million to build.

PICTURE EXCLUSIVE

DONATIONS

And we can prove that Arthur's palatial home was paid for **ENTIRELY** out of donations received by the N.U.M. during the miners' strike of 1984.

DENIALS

Despite denials from communist Scargill and his union cronies, we have traced **MILLIONS** of pounds intended for the miners' strike fund which were diverted by Scargill into secret Swiss bank accounts.

We believe the money was than smuggled to Brazil by a leading N.U.M. figure, and used to buy Nazi gold.

The Nazi gold, proceeds of Hitler's evil war crimes, was then used by Scargill to buy this £200 million luxury home.

Scargill's living room (right) is an Aladdin's Cave of priceless treasures, all paid for out of NUM funds.

The walls are lined with famous paintings. This one alone by Van Goff cost £24 million.

Scargill picked up this small vase, big enough to hold only a small flower, at Sotherbys. Price – £10 million.

This French Louis XIV waste paper basket carved from solid ivory weighs 40 tons and is worth more than its weight in gold.

Arthur's favourite chair – a Wedgewood willow pattern Queen Ann 4 legged carver also folds out into a bed. Value – £350 million.

Hand knitted foam-backed Egyptian carpets, embroidered in gold – a snip at only £3 million per square foot.

Cushion – £40 million.

Our investigators have uncovered *documentary evidence* of Scargill's illicit dealings. Airline tickets purchased in the name of 'P. Heathfield' show that the N.U.M.'s Deputy President made *SIX* return journeys from Switzerland to Brazil during 1985.

Stuck up his bottom were several rubber balloons, each *containing millions of pounds in used banknotes.*

BRAZIL

In Brazil he was met by former Nazi war criminals who exchanged the cash for gold.

Heathfield then returned to Britain in a luxury yacht belonging to Libya's Colonel Gadaffi.

ALMOND

And we also have a copy of the receipt handed to Scargill by the Barnsley builder who was paid £300 million on completing the house.

PISTACHIO

We rang the police and told them to arrest Scargill and his pinko pals, pointing out that our new evidence would put them behind bars for many years to come. But they said they were busy and asked if we'd call back later.

Monster Scargill (above) and (below) the receipt handed to him by a Barnsley builder.

HEY! DON'T CRAMP MY STILE

GLUE

Wm. Stubbs
(builder)
High Street
Barnsley

Received
From Arthur Scargill
£400,000,000
(in Nazi gold)

KINKY SEX TURN OF THE S

Mick can't get no satisfaction without wig and oven gloves

We all have our own special 'turn on', a sexy little secret that we share with our partners. Whether it's a fetish for French knickers, or a lusting for lacy lingerie, we all have our own kinky preferences. And what sends one man wild, may send another to sleep.

So what turns the stars on? For although we may not realise it as we watch TV, many of our top celebrities have unusual sexual preferences. So we decided to do some asking around to find out exactly what tickles the fancies of the rich and famous.

With a wife as beautiful as Jerry Hall, you wouldn't think millionaire Rolling Stone **MICK JAGGER** would need much to turn him on. But the ageing rocker has a kinky habit which costs him a fortune to maintain. For Jagger, 57, cannot make love to his wife unless she is wearing a wig! And not just any wig. The couple's expensive tastes mean that specially made hairpieces must be imported by the plane load from Iran, for model Jerry refuses to wear the same wig twice.

Jagger – 'oven gloves'

Hall – 'wigs'

Eccentric keep fit fanatic Jagger also insists on wearing oven gloves during the couple's raunchy sex sessions, as he believes this will stop his hands from going wrinkly.

FLAGGING

TV host **TERRY WOGAN** would have great trouble keeping his 'turn on' a secret. For the smooth talking Irishman is driven wild by the sound of bells, as many of his frustrated neighbours will testify! Wogan has even had a church bell tower built on to his £500,000 Surrey home in order to boost his flagging sex life. Chimes have been known to ring out across the local countryside at all times of the day and night, signalling to all and sundry that Terry is 'on the job'.

Tel's bells drive him bonkers!

When he's away from home, Terry still needs his nightly 'tinkle'. On one occasion whilst staying in an hotel, the loveable Irishman asked for six telephones to be installed in his room, and demanded that the night porter ring all of them constantly. Fellow residents were relieved when after six hours the ringing stopped and an order was received for two cigarettes to be sent up to the room.

UNIFORM

If you were to pass by the house of BBC holiday expert **CLIFF MICHELMORE** one evening, you'd be forgiven for thinking it was on fire. For the chances are you'd see a figure dressed in a fireman's uniform clambering in through the bedroom window. You would, in fact, be witnessing kinky

Wogan – 'bells'

Cliff's nightly sex ritual. Respected broadcaster Michelmore, 63, makes his way upstairs before ringing down to his wife and reporting a fire in the bedroom. Every night his wife faithfully dons her fireman's uniform and climbs a ladder to the couple's first floor bedroom window. Once inside the room she removes the costume and the couple enjoy an otherwise normal, healthy relationship.

Botty smack for 'bad boy' Bono

Controversial singing star **BONO** has spent a fortune earned from U2's hit records converting his bedroom into a perfect replica of an old fashioned sweet shop, in order to remind him of his childhood in Edinburgh.

SPANKED

Every night Bono dresses as a schoolboy while his wife puts on a grey wig and white apron. A strange and well-rehearsed scenario then follows in which Bono is

Michelmore – '999'

caught stealing gobstoppers and his bottom is spanked by the angry 'shopkeeper'. This play acting continues into the early hours, eventually building into a crescendo of passion which ends with the couple writhing naked in sherbet and dolly mixtures before both collapse exhausted and fall asleep.

TEN INCHES

Sports commentator and world expert on football **JIMMY HILL** can only make love in one place – a Victorian wendy house which he keeps in the attic of his detached Warwickshire home! Hill and his wife regularly cram themselves into the antique play house for electrifying sex sessions accompanied by the sound of brass bands and marching music. For another of Hill's sexual oddities is his taste for military music, and he has amassed a collection of some 1,000 dusty '78' records specifically for this purpose.

POPCORN

Early sexual experiences can greatly influence a person's sexual preferences later in life, and this has been the case with Radio One DJ

ONS ARS!

Bono – 'dolly mixtures'

Hill – 'Wendy house'

Sexy Simes' Inter-City sexpress

SIMON BATES. As a teen-ager he went to see the film 'The Railway Children' over 200 times. And it was on one of these visits to the cinema that Bates, 27, had his first sexual experience as he ate a packet of popcorn. This left such an impression on him that ever since that day the sight, sound or even the mention of a train has 'turn-ed him on', often with em-barrassing results.

AROUSED

On one occasion the DJ was late for a Radio One Road-show in York after catching a train at King's Cross and becoming aroused at Peter-borough. The train was held up for 20 minutes at Don-caster while Bates took a cold shower in the toilets on the platform.

How kinky are YOU?

Here's your chance to find out in our fun to do quiz

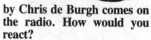

We all know how kinky the stars can be, but what about **YOU**? You could have an inner kinky-ness that you've yet to discover.
Simply answer these eight questions a, b or c, then tot up your final score to reveal you own saucy sex secrets.

1. Your car is stopped at traffic lights. What would you do?
a. Apply the handbrake, and sit patiently until they change.
b. Rev the engine till it throbs, and gently caress the gear knob.
c. Open your shirt or blouse and smear bright red lip-stick on your nipples, ad-justing the rear view mirror in order to admire your work.

2. On your regular visit to the hairdressers, do you:
a. Ask for a short back and sides.
b. Ask for a fashion cut in the style of your favourite sexy pop star.
c. Ask for you entire body to be shaved, and styling mousse to be rubbed into your parts.

3. Look at this picture. What immediately springs to mind?

a. A day on the beach at Blackpool with the family.
b. Bobbing up and down rhythmically in the saddle of a horse.
c. A rampant three-in-a-bed sex session with you, your partner and a donkey.

4. The Queen is making her annual Christmas Day speech on TV. What do you do?
a. Sit and watch patriotically, whilst enjoying a cup of tea and a mince pie.
b. Switch off the TV and watch a raunchy, 'X' rated video instead.
c. Dress up as HRH The Duke of Edinburgh, be-fore stripping naked and frottering yourself fran-tically against the fur-niture.

5. While waiting for Direc-tory Enquiries to answer the phone, how would you oc-cupy your free hand?
a. Bend a couple of paper clips until they snap.
b. Doodle on a notepad, per-haps drawing the curves of a naked human figure.
c. Lower your trousers, press the mouthpiece to your parts, and smack your bot-tom firmly with the yellow pages.

6. Shopping for meat at the butchers, what would you choose?
a. Half a pound of mince.
b. A large pork sausage and a couple of scotch eggs.
c. A small, plucked chicken and a jar of vaseline.

7. You notice that your car is dirty. What would you do?
a. Nothing, except hope that it will rain later.
b. Wash the car down your-self, then gently massage its curving bodywork with a soft chamois leather.
c. Drive to the local car wash, strip naked and climb astride the bonnet with your partner for a super soapy sex session be-neath the frothy rollers.

8. You are having breakfast in the kitchen when the romantic song 'Lady in Red' by Chris de Burgh comes on the radio. How would you react?
a. Tap your foot, and per-haps whistle along.
b. Close your eyes, sway sen-suously around the room and imagine that you are dancing cheek to cheek with gorgeous Chris him-self.
c. Strip naked, douse your entire body in butter and marmalade, stick a hot croissant up your arse and hit your parts with a stick of french bread until they go off.

How did you do?

Award yourself 1 point for each answer a, 2 points for a b and 3 for a c. Then tot up your total.

10 or less: You are sex-ually inhibited. You are ashamed of your body, and think of sex as being 'wrong' and something you shouldn't do. You are a dull, un-imaginative prude.

11 to 19: You have a reasonably healthy attitude towards sex, but you are not a saucy person. You'll be better off playing it safe, hav-ing straight sex whenever possible. Avoid the use of whips, chains and rubber ap-pliances.

20 or more: You kinky devil! You show a healthy, refreshingly open attitude towards sex. So don't be bor-ing in bed. Experiment, try wild new positions, wear ex-citing costumes, and put household items up your bot-tom. Your sex life will be re-volutionised!

"He's as tight as a Duck's arse" **Norbert Colon**

NORBERT IS OFF TO WOO THE WIDOW BULGECOFFER......
LOVE IS... THE GREATEST THING...

THE OLDEST... YET THE LATEST THING...

SLAM!

I ONLY HOPE THAT I CAN BRING...

PAT PAT

A SMALL CHILD

LOVE'S STORY TO YOOOUU!

Florist

---

20 SECONDS LATER...
CHRIST ALMIGHTY!

INTER FLOWE

I'M NOT LINING THEIR POCKETS!

BUT—
HEY! THERE'S SOME BEAUTIES IN THIS GARDEN!

HE'LL NOT MISS A COUPLE.

Prize Roses

MY LOVE FOR YOU IS LIKE A R-R-RED, R-R-RED R-R-R-OSE...

Snip!   Snip!

HMM... I SUPPOSE I'D BETTER ASK...

KNOCK KNOCK

112

'ERE. HAVE YOU GOT ANY FANCY PAPER I COULD WRAP THESE UP IN?

SHORTLY—
BLOODY HELL. THAT'S THE THANKS YOU GET FOR DOING A BIT OF GARDENING FOR SOMEONE.

AT THE WIDOW BULGECOFFER'S—
WHO WANTS TO BE A MILLIONAIRE?

I DO!

kick

DING DONG

OOH NORBERT! YOU'RE EARLY.

I COULDN'T WAIT TO SEE YOU, OH LIGHT OF MY LIFE.

WHEN WE'RE APART, I GET AN EMPTY FEELING IN MY WALLET... ER, I MEAN HEART.

OH NORBERT.

TAKE ME TO MY FAVOURITE RESTAURANT.

OH MATILDA, LET'S HAVE A QUIET NIGHT IN. JUST YOU, ME, AND THE MONEY... ER... I MEAN MOONLIGHT.

NO NO. I WANT TO GO OUT FOR A MEAL.
WELL- YOU GO ON YOUR OWN. I'LL WAIT HERE FOR YOU.

OH, YOU ARE A TEASE, NORBERT.

SO—
CHEZ LAPAGLIÉ

Cuisine du monde très agressif

GOOD EVENING WIDOW BULGECOFFER. 'OW WONDERFUL TO SEE YOU AGAIN.

HELLO EDOUARDE.

ALLOW ME TO SHOW YOU TO YOUR TABLE.

WOULD SIR AND MADAM LIKE A DRINK?

YES. TWO CUPS OF TAP WATER. AND IT'S AGAINST THE LAW TO CHARGE FOR TAP WATER IN THIS COUNTRY, YOU KNOW.

NONSENSE. YOU'LL BUY ME A BOTTLE OF SOMETHING!
I'LL GET THE LIST.

Wine List

Happy Shopper Vimco-Style Drink

MILDRED... I MEAN MATILDA... THERE'S SOMETHING I'VE BEEN WANTING TO ASK FOR A LONG TIME...

YES NORBERT...

20

SHE'S DAFT AS A BRUSH

Her cheeky smile and that toothy grin are recognised thoughout the world. And her crazy antics have had the Royal Family in stitches for almost a century.

She is of course HRH The Queen Mother, Britain's best loved grandmother, court jester to the Royals and practical joker extraordinaire. Indeed, one foreign dignitary once described her as being 'daft as a brush' after witnessing some of her after-dinner antics. They included:

* **DANCING** on the banqueting table between courses.
* **FLICKING** Yorkshire puddings at her guests.
* **PASSING** round exploding cigars after the meal.

The 'Clown Princess', as she was once described, has been a prankster since childhood. And her madcap behaviour often has fellow Royals bellowing with laughter. As one Palace insider told us, some of her zany stunts have almost become legend.

KNIGHT

"Once the Queen Mother was called upon to Knight someone. The Knight will remain nameless, but he was a civil servant, and very nervous when he arrived at the palace."

"You should have seen his face when he saw the Queen Mum standing there holding a chain saw instead of a sword. The poor fellow nearly died. Of course everyone else was in stitches".

QUEEN

Occasionally her madcap stunts can back-fire. "On one occasion she blew a five foot hole in the palace toilet wall after popping theatrical explosives down the U-bend to surprise the Queen".

BISHOP

When the charges went off, the Queen certainly got a surprise. "She couldn't sit down for a fortnight. But she eventually saw the funny side!"

ROOK

Royal watchers believe the Queen Mother's schoolgirlish behaviour is a great boost for Royal morale. As one source told us, "Being a member of the Royal family does involve a lot of dull and uninteresting work, with a lot of time spent sitting around in hotels and palaces. Practical jokes are one way of relieving the boredom and making life more bearable".

MAGPIE

Perhaps her greatest prank of all came on Coronation day in 1952. Despite the recent death of her husband King George, she turned up at Westminster Abbey dressed as a traffic warden, threatening to give the newly crowned Queen a parking ticket if she didn't shift her Royal roller.

Fred Thomson, who owns a joke shop only yards from Clarence House, admits that the Queen Mum is one of his best customers. "She's in hear most days", he told us, "either buying itching powder, flatulence tablets or clockwork teeth. Last week it was plastic dog turds. She's always up to something".

BLUE PETER

Any thoughts that at 90 the Queen Mother may have to curb her clown-like behaviour were dispelled when, at a recent birthday celebration, she pretended to choke on a fishbone. When startled guests ran to her aid she sat up, smiled, and produced a dozen boiled eggs from her mouth, followed by a goldfish, and rubber chicken. And a bunny rabbit.

'I WILL MARRY BALDY'

Julie and Frank put on a brave face as they prepare for their big day.

Brave bride Julie Johnson yesterday choked back the tears as she spoke of her plans to marry a man who is going bald.

Pretty receptionist Julie fell in love with tragic car salesman Frank Sullivan, 35, when he visited the hair transplant clinic where she works.

Frank, whose hairline has been receding since the age of 18, has been told by experts that he may be completely bald by the age of 40, except for two tufts of hair above his ears.

SWEETHEART

But 24-year-old Julie is determined to marry her stricken sweetheart despite fears that the couple's children could suffer hair loss in middle age.

TOP

Frank has undergone various treatments for his baldness, so far without success. Every day he must comb long strands of hair from the side of his head across the top. He is on the waiting list for expensive hair transplant treatment, but experts have warned him that there is only a slim chance of success.

FINGERS

But while the courageous couple send out invitations for their big day, they know that one person will not be attending the ceremony. For Julie's mother Irene has vowed never to speak to her daughter again if she goes ahead with the marriage.

Says brave bride-to-be Julie

by Billy Wank and Bob Toss

LOVE

"We're in love and that's all that matters", Julie told us yesterday. "I don't care what Frank looks like. I just want to make him happy in the short time that he has left with hair. And when Frank says, 'I do', I will be the proudest girl in the world, no matter how much hair he has or hasn't got".

The couple plan to tie the knot at St. Boswell's, Fulchester at the end of September.

*On hearing Julie's touching story, local businessman Terry Burnside donated a specially made obvious ginger wig for Frank to wear during the service. "Everyone has been marvellous", said Julie yesterday.

Say it with Flowers

Could you type this invoice for me Trina? That's the seventh can of Cherryade I've sold this week.

Trina wasn't impressed

Three more and I'll get that new Sierra the boss has promised me.

Maybe we could go for a spin together, eh? It's got alloy wheels.

Sorry Roger. I can't. I get travel sick in cars.

Travel sick eh? Oh well. Never mind.

Top sales reps at Seymour Soft Drinks, Roger Rogers and Keith Cooper were crazy about new secretary Trina Jones. But getting a date with her was proving to be impossible.

Hey! Guess who's just sold a whole **crate of Limeade!** Fancy going to the flicks to celebrate?

I'd love to Keith, but I can't. I suffer from mild epilepsy. Looking at the screen could bring on an attack.

All their approaches were thwarted by Trina's endless list of medical complaints…

I'm cooking a chicken curry tonight, and there's wine in the fridge. Fancy popping round?

No thanks. My duodenal ulcer means that spicy food is out, and I can't drink due to a kidney infection.

Trina darling. I'd like you to have these chocolates. You won't believe how expensive they were…

Sorry. Chocolate gives me migraines.

Even the boss had tried and failed…

Trina. I'm flying to Paris tonight. Fancy coming along?

We could have a romantic meal at the top of the Eiffel Tower.

Sounds nice…

But it's out of the question, Mr. Seymour. I'm **acrophobic** – scared of heights.

I see

And the mere sight of an aeroplane would be enough to give me the squirts.

Oh well, never mind.

I'll just take my wife.

23

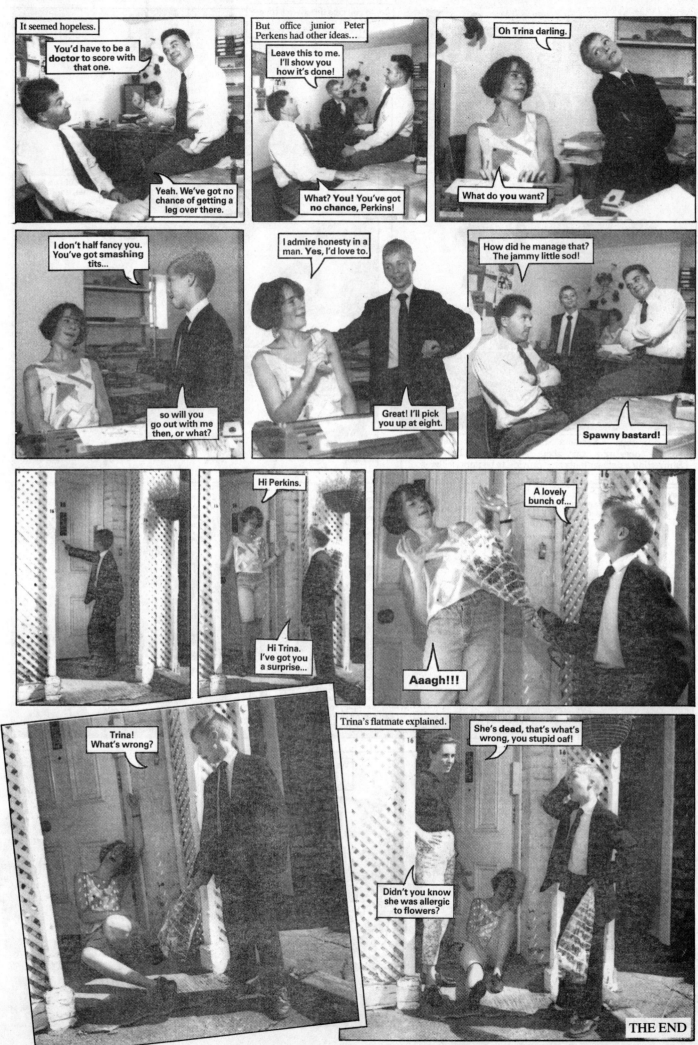

Photography by Colin D.

FARMER PALMER

'IM WERE WORRYIN' MOY SHEEP.

REMEMBER FAMILY, WHEN IN THE COUNTRY WE MUST KEEP ALL PETS ON A LEASH, CLOSE GATES BEHIND US, AND OBSERVE THE COUNTRY CODE AT ALL TIMES.

THAT'S RIGHT DAD. WE MUSTN'T SPOIL THE COUNTRYSIDE FOR OTHERS.

WHIRRRRR

WHAT'S THAT NOISE DAD?

OH, THAT'S PROBABLY THE FARMER TILLING HIS SOIL OR SOMETHING.

FOOOOOOM!
FP1

THEY TOWNIES'LL NOT BE TRESPAAAS'IN' ON MOI LAAAND AGAIN. 'OW WOULD THEY LOIKE IT IF OI CAME TO THE BIG CITY AND 'AD A PICNIC IN THEY GAAARDEN?

THAT'S ROIGHT PA.

ONE DAY SON - ALL THIS LAAND WILL BE YOURS.

DHHUR.

BUT FIRST MOY LAAD, YOU'M 'AAVE TO PROVOIDE OI WITH A GRAANDSON.

BUT PA, OI AIN'T GOT ME NO WOIFE.

OO AAR.

THAT NIGHT...

ROIGHT JETHRO, ORF YOU'M GO TO THE BAARNDANCE. OI'VE BOOKED EE A WEDDIN' FUR SATURDAY, SO GO 'N FOIND YERSELF A BROIDE.

REMEMBER TO PICK A NOICE FAT 'UN WITH BIG 'IPS.

ROIGHT PA.

WHEN YOU FOINDS 'ER YOU MUN TREAT HER NOICE LOIKE BOY. 'ERE'S FOIVE THOUSAND POUNDS OI GOT FER NOT MILKIN' NO COWS LAAST TUESDAY. DON' SPEND IT AAL AT ONCE.

OOO AAR.

11 PM... 'ALLO THERE JETHRO. 'OW YOU GET ORN AT THAT BAARNDANCE BOY?

OI FOUND ME A BROIDE PA. SHE SAYS SHE'LL MARRY OI THIS SAAAAA-URDAY.

THAT'S MOY BOY.

IS SHE PRETTY THEN JETHRO?

OI'LL SAY. HER FAATHER'S GOT NOINE THOUSAND ACRES OF PROIME AARABLE LAAND.

ROIGHT. FURST THING IN THE MAARNIN', OI BE TAKIN' EE INTO BORCHESTER TO 'AVE EE FITTED FER ONE O' THEY WEDDIN' SUITS.

OOO AAR.

SO...

HONK!
BEEP!

BLOODY TOWNIES. 'EY DON' UNNERSTAAN' COUNTRY WOYS, 'EY DON' 'AVE TER GET UP AT FOUR O'CLOCK EVRY MARNIN' TER MILK THEY CAAATLE.

ROIGHT PA

PA...

DIDN' YOU KILL ALL YOURN COOWS FER THE INSURANCE MONEY?

Borchester 35

2 MPH

AT THE TAILOR'S SHOP...

MOY BOY GETS MARRIED ON SAATURDAY. OI WANTS 'IM TO LOOK LOIKE A KING.

SHORTLY...

OI LOIKES THIS 'UN PA.

ROIGHT. OI'LL TAKES 'ER.

ON SATURDAY...

YUR SHE IS NOW JETHRO.

OOO AAAR.

'ALLO JETHRO 'ALLO PA.

JETHRO, WHOY, THIS BROIDE IS YOUR SISTER ROSIE, YER DAAAFT CLOT!

OO AAR. I THOUGHT 'ER LOOKED FAAMILIAR LOIKE. OI S'POSE THE WEDDIN'S ORF THEN. OI CAAAN'T MARRY MOY OWN SISTER, NOW CAAAN OI?

WAAAL..., IT NEVER STOPPED YER MOTHER 'N' ME, SON.

NINE MONTHS LATER...

PA! OI'VE GOT 'EE THAT GRAAANDSON YOU'M AALWOYS WAAANTED!

MOY! AIN'T 'ER GRAAND!

25

ARE YOU EUR

IN 1992 Britain is set to join the EEC. But how ready are we for this monumental move?

Recent inflammatory remarks made by one well-known politican about our European neighbours have done little to smooth the way for our entry into the Common Market. Indeed, they have sparked accusations that some of us **DON'T WANT** to be part of United Europe.

How true is this? Have we got what it takes to be **TRUE** Europeans? Come 1992 will **YOU** be dashing though the Channel Tunnel ready to greet our new European partners with open arms? Or will you be staying at home singing 'Rule Britannia', still celebrating England's victory in the 1966 World Cup Final? The answers to these 16 questions will reveal exactly how **European** you are.

1. You plan to go shopping in the morning. What steps might you take to ensure that you find a parking space in town? Would you:
a. Leave the house early to beat the rush and hopefully find a free parking meter.
b. Leave whenever you're ready, and simply hope that a parking meter is available.
c. Sneak into town at midnight and hang a beach towel on the best parking meter you can find.

2. You pop into C & A to buy a bra, but when you arrive at the cash desk you notice there is a large queue. What would you do?

a. Take your place in the queue and patiently wait to be served.
b. Put the bra back on the shelf and return later when the queue has died down.
c. Barge directly to the front of the queue and shout "Ich leber stomph das bustenholten!"

3. You are driving along the road when a car pulls out in front of you causing you to brake sharply. How would you react?
a. Drive on, perhaps tutting quietly to yourself.
b. Beep your horn at the offending motorist to let him know you're annoyed.
c. Screech to a halt diagonally across the front of the other car, leap out and bang your fists repeatedly on his bonnet, shouting: "Bastardo! Bastardo! Mamma mia! Bastardo!!"

4. You are walking along the pavement when a rather attracive woman passes by. What would you do?
a. Look away modestly, and perhaps blush a little.
b. Smile and maybe say "hello".
c. Smear a tub of Brylcream all over your head, pinch her backside then proceed to follow her around for half an hour, together with twenty of your mates, all riding on pathetic little scooters, making a variety of crude advances and suggestive remarks.

5. You're busy at work when suddenly you realise it's 12

o'clock. What do you do?
a. Have your lunch, read the paper, then return to work 45 minutes later.
b. Ignore the time and keep on working till you've finished what you're doing.
c. Sit down under a tree and go to sleep for six hours.

6. You're holidaying on the beach when you see a rather old and weary looking donkey giving rides to children. What do you do?
a. Pay no attention. It's a fairly common sight.
b. Pat the donkey on the head and offer it a sugar lump.
c. Goad it with a sharp stick, then get 100 of your friends to jump up and down on its back until it falls over and dies. Then go to sleep for six hours.

7. You wake up in the middle of the night feeling a bit peckish. What do you do?
a. Roll over and go back to sleep.
b. Pop down to the kitchen for a cup of tea and a biscuit.
c. Phone twenty of your friends and invite them to come round and spend the next five hours eating snails, frogs, onions and garlic, smoking 'Gittannes' and drinking 48 litres of wine.

8. You arrive for work in the morning. What is the first thing you do?

a. Sit in the toilet for twenty minutes reading the paper.
b. Start the day's work straight away.
c. Spend three hours shaking hands with your colleagues, hugging them and kissing them on both cheeks as through you haven't seen them for twenty years.

9. Your car is stuck behind a large, slow moving lorry which happens to be carrying live sheep. What would you do?
a. Slow down and wait patiently until a safe overtaking opportunity arises.
b. Immediately overtake the lorry at high speed and hope nothing is coming in the opposite direction.
c. Overtake the lorry, set a road block to stop it, smash the cab windows and then set fire to all the sheep.

10. There's a parliamentary election taking place in your constituency. On polling day who would you vote for?
a. A middle of the road candidate with moderate views on most issues.
b. A mainstream left or right wing politician. A socialist or a conservative perhaps.
c. A four foot tall, obviously mad, one bollocked Nazi dictator who shouts a lot and has a stupid little 'tooth brush' moustache.

OVERNIGHT PLASTIC SURGERY CENTRE

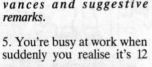

DON'T WORRY. THINGS WILL LOOK DIFFERENT IN THE MORNING

PEAN?

11. You admire your next door neighbour's lawn which is particularly well kept. Which of the following would you do?
a. Nothing. You'd be quite happy with your own patchy area of grass.
b. Ask for his advice to enable your lawn to look as good as his.
c. After promising him that you won't, move your garden fence onto his land making his lawn part of your garden. And if he complains, shoot him.

12. You are walking down the street when you see an old lady being mugged by two youths. How do you react? Would you:
a. Wade in without a thought for your personal safety and try to fight the youths off.
b. Run to the nearest telephone to call the police.
c. Ignore the fracas completely, wave a white flag above your head, then run and hide in your underground nuclear bomb proof bank vault and try to work out how much money you've got.

13. Your local football team has won a game. How would you celebrate? Would you:
a. Go out and have a few drinks with friends.
b. Just stay at home. You aren't too bothered about football.
c. Drive round in circles in a stupid little Fiat car with six people on the roof, waving your hands out of the window and honking the bloody horn all night.

14. You are playing football. At half time it suddenly dawns on you that your team is losing heavily. What action would you take?
a. Encourage your team to do better, and make more effort in the second half.
b. Just go out and enjoy the second half. After all, it's only a game.
c. Hang the captain of your team from a nearby lamp post, then go out and change sides, joining the winning team for the second half.

15. It's Saturday morning, the lawn needs a trim and the car could do with a wash. So what would you do?
a. Get up bright and early, get both jobs done, then go to a football match in the afternoon.
b. Have a lazy lie in, get up at eleven and try to do at least one of the jobs during the afternoon.
c. Buy a big box of Belgian biscuits and sit on your fat arse all day eating them.

16. It's Sunday evening, there's nothing on telly and you're bored. What would you do to pass the time?
a. Go down to the local pub, have a few beers and a sing-song with your pals, and perhaps buy a curry on the way home.
b. Rent a video, buy a few cans of beer and invite some friends round for a party.
c. Go out in your Volvo to buy some hard core pornographic magazines from the local chemists, then go home and have a wank listening to Abba records. Then kill yourself cos its Monday tomorrow.

How did you do?

Tot up your final score by awarding yourself 1 point for each answer **a**, 2 points for a **b**, and 3 for a **c**.
47 or less – You're so typically British. Obstinate, old fashioned and reluctant to change. You view all foreigners as inferior beings. Basically you're a racist. You're obsessed with past history, things like the war, which happened many years ago, and wasn't really Germany's fault anyway. You refuse to move with the times, and come 1992 you'll be well on the way to extinction, just like the dinosaurs.
48 – Well done. You're a true European, always prepared to broaden your horizons, make new friends and co-operate fully in the formation of a new Europe. The future of Britain, Europe and indeed the whole world lies at your feet.

DONG!
'Big Ben' goes *starkers*

A scene from the red hot porno flick

Pinko commie comic Ben Elton will be left red faced after being seen in the pink in a red hot blue movie soon to be released.

VIDEO

Green funny man Ben, 27, will be purple with rage when a black market video featuring the TV funny man and best selling novelist **STARKERS** goes on sale next month.

SHOCKED

During the hard core XXX rated film shocked fans will see Elton:
★ **BONKING** with a bevvy of blonde beauties.
★ **ROMPING** with a roomful of randy redheads.
★ **FIDDLING** with his parts until they go off.

SIZZLING

The sizzling on-screen sex romp was filmed in 1974 in a hotel bedroom in Hartlepool. At the time Ben, 28, was struggling to earn a living as a comic on the gritty northern club circuit. We believe he was paid £5 to perform lurid, steamy sex acts on camera.

DEVASTATED

A source close to the comic told us that Elton was "devastated" by news of the movie's pending release. "Ben was absolutely gutted when he first heard that this film has surfaced after all this time. All the hard work he's put in over the last few years could be ruined by one small mistake he made in the distant past. Everyone makes mistakes, and Ben bitterly regrets making this movie. He had hoped that this episode was all behind him."

BLACKADDER

Elton, a multi-millionaire several times over, commands fees of several thousand pounds for live appearances, and has drum-med up extra millions writing TV's 'Blackadder'. But now he is fighting to save his career, and has threatened to sue film distributors Videowank (Amsterdam) Ltd. if copies of the movie go on sale.

TWEED

The video was set for release next month, but this may be delayed while legal wrangling goes on. And if Elton's lawyers are successful, copies of the video will have to be destroyed.

CORDUROY

However, we are giving away **EXCLUSIVE** copies of the cassette **FREE** to the first 5,000 readers who can answer this simple Ben Elton question. All you have to do is tell us the name of Ben's best selling book 'Stark'. Pop your answer in an envelope together with £300 cash, and send it to 'Ben Elton Sizzling Sex Romp Naked Porno Movie Offer Competition', Viz, P.O. Box 1PT, Newcastle upon Tyne, NE99 1PT.

28

PLINK...PLINK...*FIZZ!*

Leading scientists are set to examine a miracle new source of fuel that could be set to power our cars in centuries to come.

And the revolutionary new fuel, unveiled by a Tayside man earlier this week, contains **NONE** of the harmful pollutants found in petrol and diesel fuels.

SHORTAGES

Taxi driver Murdo McGee, 58, claims he came up with the solution to the world's growing fuel shortages after years spent driving his lorry around the UK's over-crowded and polluted roads and motorways.

PROPERTIES

"I realised that what was needed was something as cheap and as readily available as water, that would have the same combustive properties as petrol, but emit no toxic fumes," Mr. McGee told us. His solution is incredibly simple.

"What I propose is that chemical companies produce some sort of tablet, about the size of a paracetamol, which when dropped into water turns it into petrol. These would be called *Petromol*."

POLLUTION

As well as providing a limitless amount of free fuel, 'Petromol' tablets will also irradicate pollution. "As well as turning the water into petrol, another chemical could be included which gets rid of all the pollution," Mr. McGee explained.

Murdo's miracle pill puts paid to petrol headache

"Surely, if we are able to put a man on the moon, it is not beyond the chemical manufacturers' abilities to come up with a simple tablet, pill or capsule that would turn water into petrol. They could be sold in shops or garages, and if they were small enough they could be kept in little plastic dispensers, like the ones 'Tic Tac' mints come in."

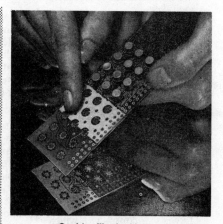

Could pills looking not unlike these electronic circuit boards provide us with the fuel of the future?

Mr. McGee told us that if the tablets were larger, they could be individually wrapped in foil and sold in boxes, like 'Alka Seltzer'.

PUFF

Mr. McGee is at present working on a new invention – an aerosol spray, one puff of which will cure cancer.

29

NO NEWS IS BAD NEWS!

BBC bosses are set to SCRAP the popular long running series 'The Nine O'Clock News' — because of outrageous cash demands by newscaster Martyn Lewis.

Angry producers have been forced to end the popular series, which has run for decades, because they can not cope with senior news reader Lewis's phenomenal wage demands.

LASHED

And other newscasters – among them Moira Stewart – wept when they heard the news. And they lashed out at Lewis, who was head hunted from ITV in order to spearhead the BBC's top news show.

One fumed: "He's forcing us all out of a job, and we're bloody mad about it."

LAVISH

Lewis's astonishing contract – offered to tempt him away from News At Ten – is thought to be the most lavish in the history of TV newscasting, netting the straight faced anchor man an amazing **£10 MILLION** a year. It includes:

★ £50,000 per show.
★ Hefty bonus payments of up to £100,000 per news bulletin, such as during the Gulf Crisis.
★ A 'signing on' fee thought to be in the region of a million pounds.
★ Enormous lump sum payments for any ideas or news items which he thinks up himself.

News staff at the BBC were outraged by a clause in Lewis's contract which allows him to write his own news if he feels the script for any particular show isn't good enough, or change any item of news which he thinks isn't good enough.

ELEPHANTS

Reporters and technicians are believed to have walked out recently after Lewis insisted on reading out a story about elephants which he had written during rehearsals.

Beeb set to axe money mad Martin

An insider told us: "A lot of work goes into researching and writing a news programme. On this occasion we had a busy schedule, with a lot of items about the Gulf Crisis to include. Suddenly Lewis announced that he had written a story about elephants, and said he wanted it as the main feature.

RESIGN

The story was all about how African elephants have bigger ears than Indian elephants. It lasted about 6 minutes." It was only when chief news reporter Kate Adie threatened to resign that Lewis gave in and agreed to drop the story – for the time being.

SPARKS

On another occasion sparks flew when Lewis insisted on reading the weather forecast. According to our insider he felt he could do a better job than John Kettley. In the end he agreed to allow Suzanne Charlton to read it, on the condition that she didn't make any mistakes."

SLADE

Falling viewing figures have raised grave financial worries, and bosses fear that the Nine O'Clock News could go bankrupt if Lewis continues to receive such incredible sums. And months of speculation will end later this month when BBC chiefs officially announce the axing of the show.

Lewis – outrageous cash demands

One bitter insider told us: "Lewis has become a law unto himself. He's money mad, and far too big for his boots. He had to be stopped, and axing the news was the only way it could be done."

COCKNEY REBEL

Publicly news chiefs deny there is any rift, and blame falling viewing figures on attractive news readers like Zenab Budawi appearing on ITV. A spokesman told us:

"Generally speaking there is less news nowadays than in the past, and we are simply streamlining our news operations. There will still be regular news bulletins on the BBC, and that programme at the weekend – the one with subtitles."

Jason King yesterday

The Nine O'Clock News slot is expected to be filled by re-runs of the popular vintage crime thriller series 'Department S' featuring Peter Wingard as Jason King.

KRANKIE UNVEILS TEST XI

Children's TV entertainer and 'Crackerjack' star Jeanette Krankie this week announced her All Time Cricket Test XI.

And there are a few surprises in four footer Jeanette's final selection.

PACE

As expected she has concentrated on pace in her attack, with no less than 3 seam bowlers spearheaded by Australia's Dennis Lillee and 'body line' bowler Harold Larwood. Yet strangely there is no room for fiery Fred Trueman or former England captain Bob Willis. Derek Underwood's selection is Jeanette's sole concession to spin.

STROKE

The opening pair of Graham Gooch and John Edrich were chosen for their dependable no-nonsense stroke play, with Australian great Don Bradman at three.

THROB

In a strong middle order Jeanette picks Farouk Engineer ahead of Kent's Alan Knott, with Pakistan heartthrob Imran Khan in at seven.

SURPRISES

Among the few surprises is the omission of Dr W.G. Grace, perhaps the greatest cricketer of all time, who only scrapes in as twelfth man.

Jeanette's team lines up as follows: Gooch, Edrich, Bradman, Viv Richards, Engineer, Dennis Compton, Khan, Sir Richard Hadlee (captain), Lillee, Larwood, Underwood and Grace.

CHEEKY CUNT

200 FOOT TESSIE'S A MONSTER DRAW

We've all heard of the Loch Ness Monster. But now tourists are being warned of another mystery monster said to lurk beneath Britain's inland waterways. In the West Midlands to be precise.

By our West Midlands Correspondent

Mr. Guthrie yesterday

And the new underwater 'discovery' is bound to be every bit as controversial as its Scottish counterpart.

BANQUET

The first sightings of 'Tipton Tessie' were made by Hugo Guthrie and his wife Elaine as they travelled home from a banquet at Tipton Town Hall where Mr. Guthrie works as a local councillor.

CANAL

"It was quite late at night, and my wife and I were just crossing the Staffordshire and Worcestershire Canal at Rowley Regis, just south of Tipton, when Elaine spotted a large, dark object moving slowly through the water."

FLIPPERS

Mr. Guthrie stopped the car and got a good look at the beast. "I'd say it was about 200 feet long, had four large flippers, and a long neck which rose out of the water. I wasn't sure, but it appeared to have several baby monsters swimming along beside it."

Mrs. Guthrie's vision of the monster

Mrs. Guthrie jumped from the car and took several flash photographs of the animal. "Unfortunately in the heat of the moment my wife forgot to remove the lens cap, and so the photographs are inconclusive. By this stage the monster had become aware of our presence, and slipped quietly out of sight beneath the waves."

SNORKEL

On subsequent visits to the site Mr. Guthrie has discovered more evidence to support his claims. "I found a large, wet footprint at the side of the A4101 at Brierley Hill, however it was a hot day and by the time I returned with my camera it had evaporated."

AQUALUNG

Mr. Guthrie expects Tipton to be flooded with hordes of monster hunters as 'Tessie Mania' grips the West Midlands. And he believes that this is good news for the local economy.

"I have already arranged for Tipton Tourist Information

Office to print a commemorative tea towel featuring a painting of the monster by my wife Elaine. We expect the initial print run of 50 tea towels to be snapped up by collectors. Indeed, the sky is the limit."

HEAVY HORSES

Mr. Guthrie also announced that Tipton Chamber of Commerce will be awarding a splendid prize of a weekend in Tipton for two to anyone who captures the monster on film. Photographs should be sent to Tipton Chamber of Commerce (Monster Photograph Holiday Weekend Competition), Tipton, West Midlands. Members of Tipton Chamber of Commerce, their friends and relatives are not eligible to enter.

IT'S A FIX!

Britain's most popular TV quiz show — watched by an estimated 25 million viewers — has been exposed as a FIX.

Long-running BBC2 smash hit show 'Call My Bluff' has been discredited by shock revelations of:

★ **CHEATING** by well-known celebrities.
★ **BRIBERY** by the show's producers.
★ **THREATS** made against competing panellists.
★ and **MURDER**.

Sacked studio cleaner Doris Tudstall decided to blow the lid off the biggest scandal in TV history after she was

Robinson – bets

Muir – threats

Gordon – tears

Hunt – coffee

sacked for smoking in the production booth.

"Every week Robert Robinson showed the contestants the answers, then went to the local bookies and placed bets on which team would win. On one occasion he won £15,000. And on another occasion he won ten times that amount."

HANNAH

Doris also told us how team captain Frank Muir regularly threatened opponents, once telling Hannah Gordon she would "end up face down in the river" if she got any questions right.

"Miss Gordon left the studio in tears," said Doris.

BARBERA

Muir is also alleged to have thrown a brick through the windscreen of a car belonging to 'Coffee Ad. King' Gareth Hunt after the former New Avengers star had correctly identified 'winnit' as being a noxious piece of faecal matter adhering to a sheep's arse.

GILBERT RATCHET

"FIXING STUFF ACROSS THE LAND, WITH A SMILE, A SPANNER, AND A HELPING HAND"

MY OLD TOOL KIT HAS JUST ABOUT HAD IT - BUT I HAVEN'T GOT THE MONEY TO BUY A NEW ONE.

HEY GILBERT! I'VE JUST DECIDED TO GIVE UP BEING A GREENGROCER AND EMIGRATE TO AUSTRALIA. I'LL GIVE YOU 50P IF YOU GET RID OF MY OLD STOCK FOR ME.

WELL THAT WAS AN EASY 50P - BUT WHAT AM I GOING TO DO WITH ALL THESE VEGETABLES?

WHAT'S WRONG, MR BROWN?

I WAS HOPING TO ENJOY A QUIET PINT AT THIS PUB - HOWEVER, THE LOUD AND OBNOXIOUS BEHAVIOUR OF THAT GROUP OF STUDENTS PREVENTS ME FROM SO DOING.

HMM.

A LARGE WOODEN BOX WITH POTATOES AND TURNIPS PASTED TO THE INTERIOR WILL MAKE AN IDEAL SOUNDPROOF BOOTH WHEREIN YOU CAN ENJOY YOUR DRINK IN PEACE.

EXCELLENT.

REWARD

DAMN IT. I AM A KEEN SEXUAL PERVERT, YET AT PRESENT AM UNABLE TO THINK OF ANY BIZZARE AND PHYSICALLY IMPROBABLE ACTIVITIES WHEREBY TO PROCURE CARNAL GRATIFICATION.

PERHAPS I CAN BE OF SOME ASSISTANCE

I JUST ATTACH A CAULIFLOWER TO THE END OF THIS LENGTH OF COILED STEEL WIRE, AND VOILA!

AN UNUSUAL AND POTENTIALLY STIMULATING EROTIC ACCESSORY!

QUICK THINKING, SON! HERE'S A FIVER FOR YOUR TROUBLE.

LATER..

:SIGH: I'D LOVE A PAIR OF PLATFORM SHOES

HOWEVER, THE ONLY ONES ON SALE IN TOWN ARE MADE OF LEATHER, AND MY STRICT VEGETARIAN PRINCIPLES FORBID ME FROM BUYING THEM.

HOLD STEADY, PLEASE.

SPLENDID! THESE IDEOLOGICALLY SOUND 'RADISH SOLES' MAKE THE PERFECT PLATFORM SHOE SUBSTITUTES!

HMM. SEVEN POUNDS FIFTY. THAT STILL WON'T BE ENOUGH FOR A NEW TOOL KIT.

HEY, YOU!

THE TABLOID PRESS LEARNED OF MY VEGETABLE-RELATED PROCLIVITIES AND, BECAUSE I AM A PROMINENT GOVERNMENT OFFICIAL, THE STORY MADE HEADLINE NEWS!

THAT CAULIFLOWER OF YOURS COST ME MY REPUTATION...

CRACK

...BUT EARNED ME A LUCRATIVE PUBLISHING CONTRACT. PLEASE ACCEPT THIS SMALL PERCENTAGE.

??

I SAY THERE, YOUNG MAN!

I'M MR BROWN'S WIFE - OR RATHER, HIS WIDOW!

IT APPEARS THAT SOMEONE SEALED MY HUSBAND IN AN AIR-TIGHT BOX WITH A NUMBER OF DECAYING VEGETABLES. HE DIED OF ASPHYXIATION SHORTLY AFTERWARDS.

CONSEQUENTLY, I AM ARRANGING THE CATERING FOR AFTER THE FUNERAL. PERHAPS YOU WOULD SELL ME THESE COURGETTES AND RUNNER BEANS?

I CAN MAKE THEM INTO A CASSEROLE, OR A QUICHE PERHAPS.

WELL, THAT'S ALL THE VEGETABLES DISPOSED OF

EMPTY

AND NOW I HAVE ENOUGH CASH TO BUY THAT TOOL KIT!

I'M SORRY, GILBERT, BUT AS AN ECCENTRIC SHOPKEEPER I CAN ONLY ACCEPT VEGETABLES IN PAYMENT FOR GOODS!

OH NO! JUST MY LUCK!

SORRY NO CASH! VEGETABLES ONLY!

HA HA HA HA HA

TOP POP MOP~TOP POT SHOT PLOT FLOPS!

Pop superstar Paul McCartney may have more money than anyone else in the world, but he also has more enemies.

That is the astonishing truth revealed for the first time in a sizzling new book published this month.

Writer Keith Twatt has spent 20 years researching his biography of the multi-millionaire ex-Beatle. In that time he has spoken to several of McCartney's former friends, and a man who once met him in the pub.

AFRAID

And as a result he believes he has unearthed the **TRUE STORY** about McCartney, a story that previous biographies have been afraid to tell.

HATED

And here, in these exclusive extracts from his book, Keith spills the beans on Britain's most hated pop star.

' McCartney's rise to fame and fortune has been real rags to riches stuff. From his childhood spent playing barefoot in the backstreets of Manchester, to the jet setting lifestyle he enjoys today.

But along the way Paul's single mindedness, determination and tight arsedness have made him enemies. Among them his former colleagues in The Beatles.

BASTARD

It was Paul who finally broke up The Beatles. He had wanted to keep all the money, but the others wouldn't let him. So Paul said he was leaving, and formed Wings instead. The others never really forgave him for that. Lennon wrote several songs about him. The best one was called 'Paul's A Bastard', but it never appeared on any records.

WIG

After the split in 1970 Paul still wasn't satisfied. He even tried disguising himself as Lennon, turning up at EMI Records in a wig and glasses trying to collect John's royalty cheques. He would stop at nothing to get money.

EXCLUSIVE

In the early seventies Wings repeated The Beatles' success, and once again the lolly was rolling in. But this time Paul was determined to keep the lot.

MINIMOOG

Originally he had asked Jools Holland out of Squeeze to join the band, to play the minimoog and do handclaps. But Holland wanted £12 a week to join Wings, so Paul got his wife Linda to do it instead, cos he didn't have to pay her.

KAZOO

Talk about tight arses. Paul really takes the biscuit. On one occasion Wings were recording the single 'Mull Of Kintyre' and Paul had hired several musicians to play the instruments on it.

STYLOPHONE

After a long day in the studio he turned round and told the trumpet player he wasn't happy with the trumpeting, and he wanted it all done again, but louder this time. The poor trumpeter had to stay behind after everyone else had gone home. Eventually he'd been blowing that hard he got dizzy and couldn't drive, so McCartney had to give him a lift home. When they got to his house mean McCartney charged him £2.20 for the lift, plus 20p for carrying his trumpet to the boot. And the poor fellow had only been paid £1.80 for playing on the record!

DISGRUNTLED

McCartney's maltreatment of his fellow musicians eventually almost cost him his life when a disgruntled former band member launched an **ASSASSINATION** attempt on the former mop topped star.

Macca attacker aimed to MURDER tight arse McCartney

'Mull Of Kintyre' had been at number one for a whole year and McCartney had pocketed all the loot. One particular member of the band wasn't happy about this, because he needed some money to buy a new pair of trousers. He asked Paul for £10, and was sacked on the spot.

TRIGGER

That night the person in question went out drinking, then bought a gun and crept into McCartney's house. As McCartney lay sleeping the bitter, booze soaked former band member pointed the gun at his head and pulled the trigger six times. It turned out that the gun had been loaded with blanks by mistake, and so McCartney, who slept through the entire incident, was unharmed.

SILVER

Together with his wife Linda, McCartney has made enemies outside of the music business, due to his strong views on animals that he has got. The couple are both vegetarians, Linda refusing even to eat fish fingers. Much of the stars' time and money is spent campaigning for animal rights. Indeed the couple have spent many weeks travelling around Britain incognito, visiting fun fairs in a campaign to prevent cruelty to goldfish. In one day alone at Nottingham Goose Fair Paul and Linda spent £184,000 on the coconut shy, winning goldfish which they then released into the River Trent. '

CHAMPION THE WONDER HORSE

Next week: The daughter of the lollipop man who once helped Paul across the road to school reveals: 'Paul hasn't visited me in 25 years'.

Keith's book, 'Portrait of a Tight Arse', is available from most booksellers, published by Bollock Press, priced £185.99.

DO YOU THINK WE OUGHT TO GET MARRIED?

HMM... THAT'S A PRETTY BIG STEP.

45

BIG VERN

ERNIE AND VERN ARE GOING FOR A WEEKEND BREAK IN SCOTLAND... AT A HOTEL... THIS IS THE PLACE. COME ON VERN. LET'S GO AND BOOK IN.

ERM... THIS WAY VERN. IT'S A TWIN ROOM. WE'D BETTER GO THERE TO CHANGE.

SHORTLY... IT'S CRIMINAL, ERNIE. THEY'VE GOT US BANGED UP LIKE BLEEDIN' SARDINES.

OH I DON'T KNOW. IT'S QUITE A NICE ROOM REALLY.

I'LL RING DOWN TO ROOM SERVICE FOR SOME SANDWICHES AND THINGS.

WHAT'S THE MATTER VERN?

YOU CAN HAVE THE BED BY THE WINDOW IF YOU'D RATHER.

LOOK AT ME ERNIE. I'M FORTY-TWO. I'VE SPENT TWENTY-EIGHT YEARS IN STIR. MY KIDS HAVE GROWN UP AND I'VE NEVER KNOWN 'EM.

THIS TIME I'M GUNNA DO ME BIRD. KEEP ME NOSE CLEAN. WHEN I GET OUT I'M GOIN' STRAIGHT ERNIE.

KNOCK KNOCK

AH. THAT'LL BE ROOM SERVICE.

YOUR TEA AND SANDWICHES SIR.

OOH LOVELY.

WOULD YOU LIKE A SANDWICH VERN?

FUCK YOU SCREW! I'M NOT EATING THIS FILTH!

OH DEAR

PTHODO!

I'M NOT LETTIN' THESE BASTARDS GET TO ME ERNIE. THEY AIN'T GUNNA GRIND ME DOWN! TO THEM I MIGHT JUST BE A NUMBER, BUT I'M A HUMAN BEING ERNIE!

WELL PERHAPS WE CAN GO DOWN TO THE RESTAURANT FOR SOMETHING TO EAT. THE BUFFET'S OPEN TILL TEN.

COME ON THEN.

WHAT ON EARTH'S THAT SMELL... VERN! WHAT ARE YOU DOING?

ONE STINKING BUCKET BETWEEN SIX MEN. IT'S SO DEGRADING.

TABLE FOR TWO PLEASE. ROOM 36.

CERTAINLY SIR.

PASS THE WORD AROUND MUSH. I'M MUSCLIN' IN ON THE SNOUT RACKET. TELL MR. BIG THERE'S A NEW FACE ON THE SCENE.

HMM.... I THINK I'LL TRY THE SMOKED SALMON IN A BASKET...

THAT'S WHAT I'M HAVING. IT'S VERY NICE. I CAN HEARTILY RECOMMEND IT, ACTUALLY.

YOU QUEER MONSTER! YOUR SORT MAKE ME PUKE!

SORRY?

HE'S A FUCKIN' NONCE ERNIE.

VERN. SIT DOWN. EVERYBODY'S LOOKING AT YOU.

IT COULD HAVE BEEN YOUR KIDS ERNIE. LET ME AT HIM. I'M GUNNA CUT HIM ERNIE!

IS EVERYTHING TO SIR'S SATISFACTION?

GET BACK ERNIE!

WHAT THE..?

I SAID NOBODY MOVE!

COME ANY CLOSER AND THE SCREW GETS IT!

34

Jimmy Hill's World of Birds' Nests and Cricket

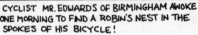

20 THINGS YOU NEVER KNEW ABOUT WOOD

Wood you believe it! Wood is back with a bang. There was a time when everything was wooden. Houses, wardrobes, shoes (in Holland) and strips on the side of certain motor cars. But in recent years the price of wood has *sawed*, and manufacturers have turned to other materials, such as plastic and tupperware, for making things out of.

A wooden table and chairs yesterday

But now wood is making a comeback, with wooden doors, drawers and cupboards more popular today than at any time in the past. Probably.
But what exactly is wood? What are the facts about this fibrous, knotty substance we see all around us? Here are twenty things you never knew about wood.

① Money doesn't grow on trees, or so the saying goes. But wood does! Believe it or not a tree is nothing more than a giant flower, made out of wood. And with leaves on it.

② Saying 'you can't see the wood for the trees' is like saying 'you can't see the school for the fish'. That's because a group of trees **IS** a wood!

③ As indeed a group of rhinocerouses is a 'crash'.

④ As indeed as well a group of gorillas is a 'flange'.

④ Cave man first discovered wood's potential as a manufacturing material, making crude wooden clubs to hit dinosaurs with.

⑤ The Queen Mother's teeth, originally a wedding gift from Sir Henry Moore to King George VI, are made entirely out of wood.

⑥ Many of today's top pop stars take their names from wood. For example Ronnie Wood. And Phil Oakey.

⑦ And so do many sports stars, like tennis player Arthur Ashe, and cricketer Derek Underwood.

⑧ We've just thought of another good one for 6. Courtney Pine.

⑨ The word 'wood' can be used twice in one sentence. For example. "Wood you pass me the wood please, Woody (out of the Bay City Rollers)". In fact that's three.

Woody out of Bay City Rollers

⑩ You might expect a bread board to be made out of bread. But you'd be disappointed. It is in fact a round, flat board for cutting bread on, made out of wood.

⑪ Similarly a cheese board is not made of cheese. But it's not necessarily made out of wood either. We know someone who's got one made of marble.

⑫ Mind you, they're *usually* made of wood.

⑬ The Gas Board is definitely not made out of wood. Rather, it is an administrative body responsible for the sale and distribution of domestic and commercial gas supplies.

⑭ The Greek word for wood is 'xylos', meaning xylophone or literally 'wooden piano'.

⑮ It may not look appetising to us, but wood is eaten and enjoyed by many animals, among them beavers, whose revolving 'saw-like' teeth can fell six trees in a minute.

⑯ Some animals don't *eat* wood, but are actually *made out of it*. For example the Wooden Horse of Troy, a large wooden horse, in Troy. And woodworms,

K £39.99
A wooden cupboard with shoes in it

small worms made out of wood.

⑰ A 'clothes horse' is *not*, as you might expect, another type of horse, made out of clothes. It is in fact an indoor washing line sort of thing... made out of wood!

⑱ And a 'saw horse' is not a horse made out of saws. In fact it's not a horse at all. But it *is* made out of wood.

⑲ A 'horse fly' isn't a horse either. It's a fly that eats horses! (But that *isn't* made out of wood.)

LeTTERbOcks

LETTERBOCKS
VIZ COMIC
P.O. BOX 1PT
NEWCASTLE-UPON-TYNE
NE99 1PT

Monarch's money misery

It's true that money can't buy you happiness. Take the Queen, for example. She's got seven billion quid, and just look at her face. The miserable old bag.

F. Cortina
Daggenham

My husband believes you should live every day as though it is your last. Consequently he has spent the last 17 years in a hospital intensive care ward, wearing an oxygen mask and with a rubber tube up his arse.

Mrs. T. Bolus
Spittle

It's always the quiet, shy ones who go beserk and gun down people on the streets. Surely it would therefore make sense if gun clubs only allowed flambouyant extroverts to join.

T. Starlet
Arbroath

Grass isn't always greener

Who said the grass is always greener on the other side of the fence? My next door neighbour's lawn is an absolute disgrace.

M. Rumming
Feltcham

I must speak out in defence of World War Two fighter pilots. Not all Battle of Britain veterans are like Wing Commander "Buffy" Beaumont (Letters, Viz 44). My father never speaks about his role in the battle. Mind you, he was shot down and killed on his maiden flight.

Mr. G. Clambeard
Leamington Spa

I'm keen on Keen

I find talented coffee actress Diane Keen rather attractive. I wonder whether she has ever got her kit off in a film, and if so, is it available on video?

V. W. Beetle
Penge

Well Mr. Beetle, the good news is that Ms. Keen got them out in the screen version of The Sweeney. The film has been released on video and should be available from most video outlets. Mind you, frankly they were nothing to write home about.

My husband used to laugh at me. For twenty-five years I've slept with a miner's helmet on. But the other night I had the last laugh when we had a power cut, and I was able to find my way to the bathroom in the dark.

Mrs. M. G. Midget
Harwich

The other day my 3-year-old son was in the bath when he suddenly cried out "Mummy. Come and look at my cock." Imagine my surprise and relief when I discovered he was referring to a small plastic cockerel belonging to his toy farm set, which he had taken into the bath with him!

Mrs. N. Bluebird
Washington

"I'm playing with my knob", shouted my 3-year-old son whilst having a bath the other day. Imagine my relief to discover the knob in question was a round, wooden one which he had removed from the bathroom door!

Mrs. N. Bluebird
Washington

I'll stick to sterling

The Government are quite right to stick to their guns and refuse to accept a single European currency. I have been saving for the last thirty years, and all my savings – over £600 – are in sterling. I'm sure there are many others like me who would lose all their savings overnight if a new currency were introduced.

Mrs. T. Herald
Workington

The last time we allowed the French to meddle with our money it all went decimal. We lost the thrupenny bit, the ten bob note, and more than sixpence in every shilling. And the price of butter doubled, as usual.

Mrs. H. Sunbeam
Kettering

"Mummy. Look at the size of my pork sword", said my 3-year-old son the other day whilst playing in the bath. Imagine my relief upon entering the room to see him playing with a toy sword which he had somehow made out of sausages.
Do I win £5?

Mrs. N. Bluebird
Washington

I'VE COME FOR THE JOB POLTFILLA-ING THIS BIT OF FENCE.

I'M SORRY. THE POST HAS ALREADY BEEN FILLED

Tropical Tracker

I thought your readers might like to know about Tropical Fruit Tracker, a delicious new combination of oats, nuts, crisped rice, coconut, pineapple and banana wrapped in moist chewy caramel. It's a tasty and filling alternative to other snack bars, the taste of tropical paradise on chilly winter days! New Tropical Fruit Tracker Bar is a perfect way to finish off a meal, or makes a substantial wholesome snack to have at any time of the day.
Tropical Fruit Tracker bars, from Mars, are now available from grocers' shops throughout the country in boxes of six. (And with only 133 calories per bar, you will be able to look fantastic in your bikini next year!)

Rebecca Leigh
Paragon Communications

If any readers require further information about the new Tropical Fruit Tracker bar they can write to Rebecca at Paragon Communications, Film House, 142 Wardour Street, London W1. And perhaps Rebecca could be kind enough to arrange for a large box of Mars confectionery to be sent to us at our usual Letterbox address.

Top Tips

IF DINING in restaurants don't start eating until every course has been brought to the table. With your whole order layed out in front of you, it is much easier to check the bill when it arrives.

F. Consul
Leeds

BRIGHTLY coloured household slippers are not only comfortable for outdoor summer wear, they also serve to distract passers-by from a toupeé, if one is worn.

M. Oxford
Ruddock

SEX T.V. FROM OUTER SPACE

Viewers will soon be sitting down to watch a new kind of satellite TV. And unlike its competitors, the new channel promises to be **out of this world**.

For scientist Trevor Rowntree claims he has successfully unscrambled the first ever television pictures broadcast by aliens from outer space.

CHANNEL

And Trevor, 42, couldn't believe his eyes when he first tuned in to the new channel. For rather than dull soaps, dreary quiz shows and dismal documentaries, the space alien channel features nothing but red-hot, non-stop, 24-hour **SEX**.

HEBRIDES

Although unsure about which planet the pictures are coming from, Trevor is convinced the new channel will be a big hit in Britain. "It's incredible", he told us. "It's raw sex. Uncensored, explicit, throbbing action. The rules about broadcasting in space must be different, because the stuff they show is unbelievable".

VIRGIN

Trevor first picked up the alien TV signal by accident, when a dustbin lid got caught on his TV aerial during a gale. "It formed a sort of space TV receiver dish", said Trevor. He has since perfected a design for a space dish, and plans to start producing them on a commercial basis. Meanwhile, he has been

Trevor set to clean up with dirty dishes

monitoring the broadcasts regularly now for several months. "All the programmes feature non-stop, no-holds-barred, blistering space sex action, with gorgeous long-legged alien women having full space sex, lesbian space sex, space bondage and other kinds of alien sex never seen before".

OUR PRICE

And Trevor believes the alien women are better looking than humans. "They're very similar to our woman, except they're better looking, with green skin, silver eyes and much bigger tits".

H.M.V.

Trevor plans to manufacture and sell his patented space TV dishes, and claims that viewers can be receiving alien sex TV by Christmas if they send him a cheque today. The dishes, priced £900, can be ordered direct from Trevor. Please send cash only to Alien Space Sex TV Ltd., 114b Balsover Avenue, Dudley, West Midlands.

Space lust! Aliens have sex on their new satellite TV channel.

Hilda's poll tax shocker

Housewife Hilda Harper got the shock of her life when she opened a Poll Tax demand from her local council in Goole, Humberside.

WAR

The bill demanded a Community Charge payment of £395 in the name of Hilda's grandfather Thomas Harper. Hilda couldn't believe her eyes, for her grandfather hasn't lived in the house since 1942 when he was killed in the war.

"At first I was angry. It's such an insensitive thing to do. But now I'm worried that I'll have to pay. And I haven't got a clue where the money will come from".

ERROR

A spokesman for Goole council yesterday apologised for the error, and assured Mrs. Harper that the bill would be cancelled. "It's just a computer error and we're sorry if it has caused any distress".

Meanwhile, Mrs. Harper insists that she won't pay a penny of the bill. "They can take me to the highest court in the land, and I still won't pay a penny", she said yesterday, before barricading herself in her 2 bedroom council house.

Keep off the nuts this Christmas

If you're going to be driving this Christmas, stay off the nuts.

That's the shock warning being issued by convicted drink/driver Frank Parkington, after magistrates slapped a 2 year ban on him and fined him £200 for driving with three times the legal limit of alcohol in his blood.

RESERVATION

Parkington, 36, was stopped by police after driving the wrong way up a dual carriageway, crashing through the central reservation and driving 60 miles per hour in a pedestrian precinct. Despite being found guilty, Frank still maintains his innocence.

TEEPEE

"As I explained to the police, I'd deliberately stayed low that night 'cos I knew I was driving. I'd only had 6 or 7 pints, and a couple of shorts. I know my limit". But Frank claims that before he left the pub, he was offered some peanuts.

"I had a couple of packets, and the next thing I knew I was feeling drowsy. It was definitely the nuts that did it. People warn you about drink/driving, but they never warn you about the nuts.".

TOMAHAWK

Frank believes a rare allergic reaction to peanuts causes his blood to turn to alcohol. But magistrates were unimpressed by his claim and found him guilty – his third similar conviction in the last six years.

"It's bloody infuriating, but what can I do? In future if I go out for a pint, I'll just have to lay off the nuts altogether".

We rang crazy drink/driving comic Jim "Nick Nick' Davison for his comment, but he wasn't in.

LEAVE one curtain open for every pint of milk you require in the morning.
Austin Cambridge
Southwick

IF YOU get to the supermarket checkout only to find you've left your purse at home, avoid embarrassment by pretending to have a nosebleed. Invariably one of the assistants will help you to the lavatory where you can remain until the store has closed.
Mrs. F. Anglia
Anglia

DON'T answer your front door. It could be burglars.
Mr. F. Corsair
Bridgenorth

WHEN out driving always turn left. Then, should you become lost, you can find your way home by reversing the procedure and always turning right.
B.M.W. Five-Series
Aldershot

MAKE everyone think you wear glasses by making a mark on the bridge of your nose with a teaspoon every morning.
Morris Minor
Coventry

WHENEVER you introduce a new system for ordering milk, make sure you explain it to the milkman beforehand.
Austin Cambridge
Southwick

Billy the Fish

DESPITE BEING BORN HALF MAN/HALF FISH, BILLY THOMSON HAS MADE THE FULCHESTER UTD NO. 1 SHIRT HIS OWN...

BUT NOW HE HAS TURNED HIS BACK ON THE CLUB IN ORDER TO GO TO BED WITH KYLIE MINOGUE IN HER AUSTRALIAN LOVE NEST.

THE NEXT DAY, BILLY ARRIVES IN AUSTRALIA...

I CAN'T BELIEVE IT. IT'S ONLY A MATTER OF SECONDS TILL I GO TO BED WITH KYLIE MINOGUE.

I'M QUIVERING ALL OVER.

HELLO. KYLIE MINOGUE SPEAKING. WHO IS IT?

IT'S ME. BILLY.

I'M HERE TO GO TO BED WITH YOU, AS PER OUR TELEPHONE CONVERSATION.

OOH BILLY! I'LL BE RIGHT DOWN!

KYLIE!

STRUTH! WHO ARE YOU?

WHY, I'M BILLY THOMSON. YOU WANTED TO GO TO BED WITH ME, REMEMBER?

BILLY THOMSON?

I WANTED TO GO TO BED WITH BILLY IDOL. I MUST HAVE GOT THE WRONG NUMBER.

OH NO!

SO... THERE'S NO CHANCE OF YOU GOING TO BED WITH ME AFTER ALL?

HA! YOU SHOULD BE SO LUCKY. I DON'T EVEN SLIGHTLY FANCY YOU. YOU'RE A FISH.

SLAM!

SNIFF

MEANWHILE, ON THE OTHER SIDE OF THE WORLD, AT FULCHESTER STADIUM, THE SECOND HALF GETS UNDERWAY... WITHOUT BILLY.

PHEEP!

AND THE EMPTY FULCHESTER GOALMOUTH IS SOON UNDER ATTACK

THIS BREAK COULD BE DANGEROUS!

YES. THIS LAD LOOKS A BIT TASTY.

HAVING NO KEEPER LEAVES OUR GOAL VULNERABLE TO ATTACK.

YES. WE'RE LOOKING A BIT THIN IN THE 6-YARD BOX.

AN OPEN GOAL! HE CANNOT MISS!

TWO-NIL TO ROSSDALE SURELY!

BUT WHAT'S THAT IN THE SKY - ABOVE OUR HEADS?

WHY! IT CAN'T BE!

IT IS!

GO! DISCS GO!

IT'S BILLY THE FISH!

AND HE'S JUST IN TIME TO SAVE THE DAY!

HOORAH!!

A REMARKABLE SAVE, EH BOSS. THE LAD TRAVELLED ALL OF 12,000 MILES, THEN PARACHUTED OUT OF A JUMBO JET TO PUSH THAT ONE ROUND THE POST!

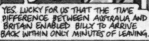

YES. LUCKY FOR US THAT THE TIME DIFFERENCE BETWEEN AUSTRALIA AND BRITAIN ENABLED BILLY TO ARRIVE BACK WITHIN ONLY MINUTES OF LEAVING.

FORTY MINUTES LATER AND THE SCORE REMAINS 1-0 TO ROSSDALE...

THE GAME APPEARS TO BE SLIPPING OUT OF FULCHESTER'S GRASP.

I WONDER WHETHER TOMMY BROWN HAS AN ACE LEFT UP HIS SLEEVE...

YES. A STRANGE NEW SIGNING PERHAPS. SOMEONE THAT HE HAS OMITTED TO MENTION SO FAR.

TIME TO INTRODUCE A FRESH PAIR OF LEGS, EH BOSS?

YES, SYD... FOUR LEGS ACTUALLY!

BUT BOSS - WE'VE ONLY GOT ONE SUBSTITUTE LEFT... HE'S UNDER THAT TARPAULIN OVER THERE.

?

YES SYD. ONE SUBSTITUTE, FOUR LEGS!

I'D LIKE YOU TO MEET MY NEW SIGNING...

?

...WING AND WONG, THE WANG TWINS INCREDIBLE FOOTBALLING SIAMESE TWINS JOINED AT THE HIP SINCE THE AGE OF TWO.

GO! DISCS

THE SUBSTITUTION IS MADE...

THE 4-LEGGED TWINS IMMEDIATELY BEGIN TO MAKE THEIR MARK...

CRUMBS! LOOK AT THOSE ORIENTAL MARVELS MOVE!

YES. THEY'RE LITERALLY RUNNING RINGS ROUND ROSSDALE'S DEFENCE.

BLOWN FOX - YOU HAVE BALL.

IS THIS THE END FOR FULCHESTER? IS EVERYONE GOING TO PRISON? DON'T MISS THE NEXT EPISODE - BROUGHT TO YOU BY GO! DISCS PURVEYORS OF FINE QUALITY 'POP' AND 'BEAT' MUSIC TO TODAY'S YOUNGER GENERATION.

ROGER MELLIE

THE MAN ON THE TELLY

LADIES AND GENTLEMEN...

LETS HEAR IT FOR YOUR HOST ROGER MELLIE!

ROGER tonight

CLAP

THANK YOU... THANK YOU...

APPLAUSE! APPLAUSE!

APPLAUSE! APPLAUSE!

YOU'RE TOO KIND

WELL, WHAT A WEEK IT'S BEEN FOR NEWS EH? MICHAEL ASPEL REVEALED THAT HIS FAVOURITE DRINK IS TEA...

PERHAPS THAT'S WHY HE'S GOT BAGS UNDER HIS EYES!

HA HA HA HA! HO HO HO HO!

LAUGH

AND I SEE DAVID BELLAMY HAS BOUGHT A NEW HOUSE.

MUST BE A... WHAT'S THAT? AH!.. GREENHOUSE!

HO HO!

MUST BE A GREENHOUSE

HA HA HA HA!

ON WITH THE SHOW, AND WHAT A **STONKER** OF A SHOW WE HAVE TONIGHT!

MY FIRST GUEST IS AN M.P. WE ALL KNOW AND LOVE...

ARE YOU **SURE** THIS IS A GOOD IDEA GIVING ROGER A LIVE CHAT SHOW THREE NIGHTS A WEEK TOM?

DON'T WORRY SIR. ROGER'S BEEN WONDERFUL IN REHEARSALS. HE'S A NEW MAN, I CAN ASSURE YOU

I JUST HOPE HE DOESN'T INADVERTENTLY UPSET ANY OF THE GUESTS...

YOU KNOW HOW TOUCHY SOME PEOPLE CAN BE

LADIES AND GENTLEMEN, PLEASE WELCOME...

CECIL PERKINSON!

NOW THEN, MR. PERKINSON, YOU'RE THE MAN WHO'S BEEN CHARGED WITH THE SOMEWHAT AWESOME TASK OF OVERSEEING THE PRIVATISATION OF OUR RAILWAYS

YES, AND IT'S A CHALLENGE THAT I'M LOOKING FORWARD...

HEY! WAIT A MINUTE! YOU'RE THE ONE WHO GOT THAT BIRD UP THE STICK, AREN'T YOU!

I BEG YOUR PARDON?!

YEAH! YOU WERE SHAGGING YOUR SECRETARY, THAT'S IT. SARAH SOMEBODY. SHE GOT PREGNANT

I DON'T REALLY THINK...

IF WE COULD JUST TALK ABOUT THAT FOR A MOMENT

I'M SORRY. I'D MUCH RATHER...

TELL ME, WHAT EXACTLY HAPPENED? AN ACCIDENT WAS IT? BALLOON BURST OR WHAT?

I'LL TELL YOU SOMETHING. IT'S WORTH FILLING THE BUGGERS WITH WATER FIRST, TO CHECK FOR LEAKS

REALLY! THIS IS AN OUTRAGE!

YEAH, I'VE HAD A FEW CLOSE SHAVES MYSELF. MESSY BUSINESS IT IS TOO.

MIND, IF YOU ASK ME IT'S THE BIRDS WHO SHOULD TAKE THE PRECAUTIONS.

IF THEY GET UP THE DUFF THEY'VE ONLY GOT THEMSELVES TO BLAME

CHRIST ALMIGHTY! GET HIM OFF!! QUICKLY, **PULL THE PLUG!!**

HALF AN HOUR LATER...

WELL, THAT'S ABOUT ALL FOR TONIGHT'S SHOW. SORRY ABOUT CECIL, PISSING OFF EARLY. MISERABLE OLD SOD.

I'LL BE BACK SAME TIME ON WEDNESDAY, SO UNTIL THEN IT'S GOODNIGHT FROM ME

GREAT SHOW EH TOM? CAN'T WAIT TO SEE THE VIEWING FIGURES

PROBABLY SOMETHING LIKE TEN MILLION. WHAT DO YOU RECKON?

NO ROGER. I'M AFRAID NOBODY SAW THE SHOW. FOR THE LAST HALF HOUR VIEWERS HAVE BEEN WATCHING TOM AND JERRY CARTOONS

AND THE DIRECTOR GENERAL WANTS TO SEE YOU RIGHT AWAY

SHORTLY...

YOU WANTED TO SEE ME?

YES ROGER. HAVE A SEAT

TOM TELLS ME THERE WAS A BIT OF A COCK UP ON TONIGHT'S SHOW. SHAME ABOUT THAT. IT WAS THAT PERKINSON FELLA WASN'T IT. DULL AS FUCK HE WAS

THERE'S NOT A LOT YOU CAN DO WITH A BORING BASTARD LIKE THAT, IS THERE

MIND YOU, IF WE SPENT A BIT MORE ON THE OLD **HOSPITALITY** - GET THE GUESTS PISSED UP A BIT BEFORE THEY GO ON - I THINK THAT'LL MAKE A BIG DIFFERENCE

SHUT UP WILL YOU ROGER, AND LISTEN. THIS IS IMPORTANT.

YOU ARE FIRED, DO YOU UNDERSTAND? YOUR SHOW IS CANCELLED. YOU DO NOT WORK HERE ANYMORE. IS THAT CLEAR?

NOW GET OUT

AND NEVER SET FOOT IN THESE STUDIOS AGAIN

A FEW DAYS LATER...

GOOD MORNING. I'VE GOT AN APPOINTMENT TO SEE ROGER

TAKE A SEAT WILL YOU. MR MELLIE WILL BE WITH YOU IN A MOMENT

ROGER. THERE'S A BLOKE HERE TO SEE YOU

OOH! ROGER. STOP IT! GERROFF! YOU DIRTY OLD SOD

TEE HEE HEE HEE!

OOOH! HEE HEE HEE HEE!

TEN MINUTES LATER...

YOU CAN GO IN NOW

ROGER?

OH, HI TOM!

SORRY TO KEEP YOU WAITING. JUST GIVING THE SECRETARY A QUICK BIT OF DICK-TATION!

SO WHAT'S ALL THIS THEN? A BIG OFFICE, A SECRETARY... YOU'VE GONE UP IN THE WORLD HAVEN'T YOU?

THIS IS 'MELLIEVISION' TOM. MY OWN T.V. PRODUCTION COMPANY

INDEPENDENT PRODUCTION. THAT'S WHERE THE MONEY IS!

FUCK THE BBC AND ITV. I JUST MAKE THE PROGRAMMES MYSELF, FLOG 'EM, AND BINGO! I KEEP ALL THE LOOT.

THEY'RE ALL AT IT. TAKE THAT LANKY TWAT WITH THE BIG SUITS. HE KNOCKS UP A SHOW ON THE CHEAP - PILE OF SHITE - THEN FLOGS IT TO CHANNEL 4. AND THE DAFT CUNTS PAY A BLEEDIN' FORTUNE FOR IT.

PIECE OF PISS TOM. LIKE FALLING OFF A LOG. AND IT'S A LICENSE TO PRINT MONEY!

SO... ER... WHAT SORT OF PROGRAMMES WILL YOU BE MAKING ROGER?

FUNNY YOU SHOULD SAY THAT

I'VE GOT THIS GREAT IDEA... WHISKY?

SEE THIS BOOK TOM. 'AROUND THE WORLD IN 80 DAYS'. IT'S BY THAT FAWLTY TOWERS MICHAEL WOTSIT

BLOKE...

YES, I'VE READ IT ACTUALLY

YEAH. ME N'ALL. RIGHT LOAD OF TOSS, ISN'T IT. BUT AT SIXTEEN QUID A THROW, HE MUST BE COINING IT IN

HMM... IT'S A BEST SELLER

WELL THAT'S IT, ISN'T IT. WE'LL HIT THE FUCKIN' JACKPOT! WE MAKE A TELLY PROGRAMME, THEN DO A BOOK!

BUT WHAT IS YOUR IDEA? WHAT WILL THIS PROGRAMME OF YOURS BE ABOUT?

YOU'LL LOVE THIS...

AROUND THE WORLD IN EIGHTY LAYS!

IT'S BRILLIANT. WE GO ROUND THE WORLD, RIGHT? AND I SHAG A BIRD IN EVERY COUNTRY

IT'LL MAKE GREAT T.V., AND THE BOOK WILL SELL LIKE HOTCAKES!

I CAN SEE IT NOW, EIGHTY TARTS, ALL IN NATIONAL DRESS, STRIPPING OFF FOR A BIT OF FUN WITH YOURS TRULY

FULL COLOUR PHOTOS IN THE BOOK. ADULTS ONLY! PHOAR!! WHAT DO YOU RECKON?

THAT WOULD BE UNBROADCASTABLE. PORNOGRAPHY. THE T.V. NETWORKS WOULDN'T TOUCH IT

HMMM...

TOO HOT TO HANDLE EH? MAYBE YOU'RE RIGHT

OKAY. HOW ABOUT THIS THEN. A WILDLIFE DOCUMENTARY!

LIKE OLD DICKIE ATTENBURG. 'THE TRIALS OF LIFE' - I BET THAT'S A NICE LITTLE EARNER

OH COME ON ROGER! IT COSTS A FORTUNE TO PRODUCE A PROGRAMME LIKE THAT

AND BESIDES, WHAT TRAINING HAVE YOU HAD IN ZOOLOGY?

FUCK ZOOLOGY TOM. I'M TALKING ABOUT ANIMALS. I COULD MAKE A PROGRAMME LIKE THAT BLINDFOLD!

WE COULD DO IT THIS AFTERNOON. COME ON TOM. ARE YOU IN OR WHAT?

LATER, AT THE ZOO...

HEY TOM! OVER HERE. GET A LOAD OF THIS. THESE TWO ARE SHAGGING!

REPTILE HOUSE

DO NOT FEED THE ANIMALS

TRAFFIC WARDENS CAN'T GET IT UP

Britain's army of traffic wardens are notorious for taking a hard line when it comes to minor parking offences. But when it comes to sex they're SOFT, and that's official.

For a report published this week reveals that 9 out of 10 male traffic wardens are unable to achieve an erection. And while everyone else enjoys raunchy, energetic sex with their partners, Britain's pathetic parking prefects are left to wander the streets, sticking little parking tickets on car windscreens.

INABILITY

Research shows a direct link between the issuing of parking tickets and an individual warden's inability to 'get it up', as Professor Morris McEwan-Scotch, author of the report, explains.

FRUSTRATED

"The worse a traffic warden is in bed, the more tickets he dishes out. He becomes frustrated, and angry, and inevitably he takes it out on innocent motorists."

AFFAIR

The professor refutes the suggestion that many of our traffic wardens are happily married, and enjoy normal sex lives. "This is simply not true", he told us. "My research has shown that 98% of traffic wardens' wives are having an affair with their next door neighbour, because their husbands cannot satisfy them".

VIRGINS

Professor McEwan-Scotch believes the problem of impotent traffic wardens is deep rooted. "Traffic wardens are without exception social inadequates who ideally would have liked to be policemen. Most of them are still virgins when they start the job, and they can't take their drink either. Add to this the fact that they are almost to a man *deeply* unattractive, and you can see how the problem develops."

EXCITEMENT

The professor goes on to cite various unhealthy sexual practices to which he believes traffic wardens turn in order to achieve excitement. "I have evidence which suggests up to half of Britain's traffic wardens are 'cross dressing' – wearing women's clothing – during the evening. And I am convinced that the vast majority of them use battery operated devices in the privacy of their own homes"

FOREPLAY

One of our reporters, posing as an attractive female motorist, invited a passing traffic warden to have sex in the back of his car. However, after almost thirty minutes of unimaginative foreplay the traffic warden was still unable to achieve an erection. At this point our reporter made his excuses and left.

CLAMP DOWN

Professor McEwan-Scotch wants the Government to clamp down on traffic war-

Nine out of ten are a FLOP in bed

dens, sacking them all and abolishing parking meters. "I have sent my report to the Ministry of Transport and am awaiting a reply". Professor McEwan-Scotch was recently fined £16 for parking on a double yellow line while shopping near his home.

Pitiful sight – a lonely traffic warden wanders the streets yesterday.

Farmer Jack's poll tax shocker

Farmer Jack Johnson could hardly believe his eyes when he opened a Poll Tax bill sent to his farm by the local council at Coniston in the Lake District.

BILL

For the bill included a £512 Community Charge for one of Jack's employees. Nothing odd about that, until you realise that the employee concerned is none other than George, Jack's faithful Border Collie sheepdog.

SWEENEY

"I was flabbergasted. It's bad enough me and my wife having to pay. But with another £512 for the dog, we simply couldn't afford to make ends meet".

Jack decided the only way to avoid paying the bill was to shoot George, his faithful companion of 15 years, in the back of the head. "It broke my heart, but it was either that or paying up".

Z-CARS

The next day the local council wrote apologising for their mistake, and cancelling the bill which had been issued in error. The mistake occurred because Mr. Johnson had entered the dog's name on his Community Charge registration form, a spokesman explained.

Mr. Johnson is now contemplating suing the council for damages, together with the cost of the dog and six shotgun cartridges.

MILLIE TANT

WE ARE ONE SISTERS

AND HER RADICAL CONSCIENCE

 AND NOW ON CHILDREN'S BBC, THE NATIVITY PLAY, PERFORMED BY SAINT DAVE'S SCHOOL OF FULCHESTER ROAD.

TCHOH!

 THE NATIVITY PLAY IS A DELIBERATELY MANUFACTURED VEHICLE, THE PURPOSE OF WHICH IS THE REPRESSION OF THE SEXUALITY OF SINGLE PARENT WIMMIN... AND GAY MEN.

 WHAT WAS THAT MILLIE?

OH GOD JANE! YOU MAKE ME VOMIT! YOU NEVER LISTEN TO A WORD I SAY! YOU KNOW, AT TIMES I HAVE MY DOUBTS ABOUT YOUR COMMITMENT TO LESBIANISM.

MILLIE. YOU KNOW I'M NOT A LESBIAN.

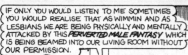

 IF ONLY YOU WOULD LISTEN TO ME SOMETIMES YOU WOULD REALISE THAT AS WIMMIN AND AS LESBIANS WE ARE BEING PHYSICALLY AND MENTALLY ATTACKED BY THIS PERVERTED MALE FANTASY WHICH IS BEING BEAMED INTO OUR LIVING ROOM WITHOUT OUR PERMISSION.

 IT'S JUST SOME KIDS DOING THE NATIVITY, MILLIE.

OH, THAT'S ALL IS IT?! THAT IS ALL? OBVIOUSLY UNKNOWN TO YOU JANE, YOUR MIND HAS BEEN SAVAGELY RAPED BY THE GROSSLY TWISTED EVIL MINDS OF MEN, WHO'S ONLY AIM IS TO DENY YOU-BY ANY MEANS - YOUR RIGHT TO BE A LESBIAN.

 OH FOR GOD'S SAKE! I'M GOING OUT!

SLAM!

 WHAT YOU DON'T REALISE JANE, IS THAT HETEROSEXUALITY WAS INVENTED BY MEN SIMPLY IN ORDER TO DENY WIMMIN ACCESS TO THE FACTS ABOUT CENSORSHIP OF THE MEDIA AND TO THUS CREATE THE MYTH OF THE NUCLEAR ARMS RACE.

 AS WE ALL KNOW JANE, IF MEN DIDN'T HUNT WHALES THEN THE GOVERNMENT WOULD BE FORCED TO STEP DOWN AND ALLOW WIMMIN TO RUN THIS COUNTRY AS A SOCIALIST LESBIAN WHOLEFOOD COLLECTIVE IN WHICH...

 TWO HOURS LATER...

I'M BACK!

... AND FURTHERMORE, JANE, IF YOU HAD ONE OUNCE OF UNDERSTANDING ABOUT THE WIMMINSTRUGGLE, YOU'D KNOW AN ULTRA-HARD-LEFT MILITANT FEMINIST RADICAL POLICY OF SEX-TERRORISM THROUGH ANTI-SELF GRATIFICATION SEXUAL DENIAL IS THE ONLY WAY TO A WORLD TOTALLY FREE OF THE MAN-MENACE, WHICH AS YOU KNOW JANE IS WHAT WE ALL WANT AS WIMMIN... AND LESBIANS.

 LATER STILL...

DING! DONG!

HMH!

 YES!!... WELL, WHAT DO YOU WANT!?

GASP!

 HO! HO! HO!... ERM... I'M FATHER CHRISTMAS.

FATHER CHRISTMAS!? FATHER CHRISTMAS?! HUH! YOUR MINDS HAVE BEEN TAMPERED WITH SINCE BIRTH!

 LISTEN TO YOUR HEARTS CHILDREN! LOOK DEEPER THAN THIS PHALLIC TRICKERY!

 AND YOU... BOY! THERE IS STILL TIME FOR YOU TO CRY OUT FROM WITHIN YOURSELF AND REJOICE THROUGH YOUR TRUE GAY SELF... COME ON CHILDREN, SING WITH ME...

GULP!

 WE ARE WIMMIN, WE ARE STRONG!

I'M SCARED.

 BUT MISSUS, WE CAME CAROL SINGING, - WE'RE SUPPOSED TO SING TO YOU!!

YES! YES! SING OUT CHILDREN! SING TO ME A SONG, A SONG CELEBRATING YOUR SEXUALITY AND POLITICAL DREAMS.

 GOOD KING WENSLESLASS LOOKED OUT, ON THE FEAST OF STEPHEN, WHEN THE SNOW LAY ROUND...

 KING? STEPHEN? LET ME SEE THIS!

HEY! GIVE US THAT BACK MISSUS - I'LL TELL ME DAD!

WHIP!

 I SHALL HAVE TO RE-WRITE THIS, BEFORE IT DAMAGES YOUR MINDS ANY FURTHER!

 HMMPH! THAT'S BETTER... GOOD LESBIAN PEOPLE'S REPRESENTITIVE WENSLESLASS LOOKED OUT, ON THE FEAST OF LESBOS...

IS THIS THE HOUSE, PET?

Mrs Brady OLD LADY

Panel 1: AW DAD. DOES GREAT AUNT ADA HAVE TO COME TO OUR HOUSE FOR CHRISTMAS AGAIN?
YES KEVIN.
OH DEAR.
IT'S THE SEASON OF GOODWILL - AND SHE DOESN'T HAVE ANYONE ELSE YOU KNOW.

Panel 2: BUT HER TEETH CLICK.
YES. AND SHE SMELLS OF WEE.

Panel 3: THAT'S ENOUGH! I'M GOING TO PICK HER UP NOW. AND I WANT YOU TO BE NICE TO HER WHEN WE GET BACK.

Panel 4: SHORTLY...
KNOCK KNOCK

Panel 5: KNOCK KNOCK
KN KN KNOCK KNOCK

Panel 6: AUNTIE ADA! AUNTIE ADA!
IT'S ME - DEREK!

Panel 7: AUNTIE ADA! I KNOW YOU'RE IN THERE. PLEASE OPEN THE DOOR!

Panel 8: COME ALONG. ARE YOU READY? OOH. IT'S BITTER OUT HERE.
I'LL BE RIGHT WITH YOU SIDNEY. THERE'S SOMEONE AT THE DOOR.

Panel 9: SLAM! CLICK CLICK CLUNK K-CHINK SLIDE

Panel 10: HALF AN HOUR LATER...
AUNTIE ADA!

Panel 11: P-P-PLEASE OPEN TH-THE D-D-D-DOOR!

Panel 12: WHERE HAVE YOU BEEN? I'VE BEEN WAITING FOR HOURS!
YOU DON'T WANT ME TO COME REALLY.

Panel 13: AND I'LL TELL YOU NOW, I DON'T WANT TO COME! THERE. I'M ONLY DOIN' THIS OUT OF THE GOODNESS OF ME HEART.
YES ADA.

Panel 14: IS THIS A NEW CAR THEN. YOU'RE LUCKY YOU CAN AFFORD IT. MY SIDNEY'S GOT A CAR YOU KNOW. OF COURSE YOU DIDN'T NEED A LICENCE IN THEM DAYS.
MY SIDNEY NEVER HAD A CAR YOU KNOW. IT WAS BLACK.

Panel 15: NOW AUNTIE - ARE YOU SURE YOU'VE REMEMBERED EVERYTHING?
YES. YES. THAT'S RIGHT.

Panel 16: 10 MINUTES LATER...
NEARLY THERE NOW, ADA. VERA AND THE KIDS ARE SO LOOKING FORWARD TO SEEING YOU...
OH DEAR.

Panel 17: I THINK I'VE LEFT ALL THE GAS ON!

Panel 18: (car making a U-turn)

Panel 19: IT'S ALRIGHT ADA! YOU'RE NOT ON GAS.
YES. YES. THAT'S RIGHT.

Panel 20: 10 MINUTES LATER...
EEH! I THINK I'VE LEFT ME BATH RUNNING!
SCREECH!
ETC. ETC.

Panel 21: FOUR HOURS LATER...
DEREK! WHERE ON EARTH HAVE YOU BEEN?
JESUS!!
I'LL TELL YOU LATER.

Panel 22: WELL IT'S LOVELY TO SEE YOU ADA.
OH YES. WELL - IT'S A PITY YOU DIDN'T WANT TO SEE ME AT YOUR WEDDING ISN'T IT! I'LL NEVER FORGIVE YOU FOR NOT INVITING ME.
BUT ADA...!

Panel 23: NEVER!! YOU CAN TAKE ME STRAIGHT HOME! I'LL NOT STAY HERE A SECOND LONGER. COME ALONG SIDNEY. I KNOW WHEN I'M NOT WELCOME!
BUT ADA - YOU WERE THERE! YOU SAT NEXT TO DOLLY - REMEMBER?

Panel 24: ANYWAY, LET'S HAVE A CUP OF TEA. THEN YOU CAN OPEN YOUR PRESENTS.
I DON'T WANT YOUR PRESENTS. I KNOW WHAT YOU'RE AFTER - WELL, YOU'RE NOT GETTING IT.

HIGHWAY TO HEAVEN

Young student Laura Lewis had decided to spend her Christmas holidays hitch-hiking across America.

As she left for the airport Laura's mother waved goodbye.

Now you be careful in America Laura

Okay mum. See you later.

Several hours later Laura's plane arrived in the USA.

We are now landing in America

In the airport foyer…

Excuse me. Where's the nearest road?

I'm going to hitch-hike my way across the USA

Why, the inter-state freeway is over that-a-way, ma'am

Here we are. I'd best get started then!

ROUTE 66

Half an hour passed by with no sign of any cars.

No luck yet. At this rate I'll never get to Miami

Ah! Here's a car. My luck's changing.

Yes… I think he's going to stop…

48

AAAAGH!

Whack!

Try walkin' on the sidewalk, Goddam son'f'a'bitch!

The car sped away at high speed, leaving Laura lying by the roadside.

It was some time later when Laura eventually awoke.

Ooh! My head. I must have been out for hours!

Mind you, I'm lucky to be in one piece. Careless drivers!

Hours seemed to drift by with still no sign of a car.

It looks like I've picked the quietest road in America. I'll never get a lift at this rate

Ah! At last! I think I'm in luck

Sure enough, the enormous, gleaming automobile pulled to a halt.

Hooray! He's stopping

The door swung open.

It's very kind of you to stop

Without a word from the driver the car pulled off.

The End

Photography by C. W. Davison

50

ARSES ON PEWS!

A controversial vicar is calling for dramatic changes in the way churches operate. For unless drastic steps are taken, he fears we could soon be witnessing the end of Christianity itself.

And vicar Dennis Randall believes that unless Holy men are prepared to move with the times, they will soon be left preaching to rows of empty pews.

PACKED

Christmas has traditionally meant big business for the churches, with standing room only in packed houses throughout the country. But all that is changing, and this year vicars are bracing themselves for record low attendances.

FALL

Over the last few years there has been a dramatic fall in the number of people going to church. And religious chiefs fear that unless action is taken to stop the rot, thousands of churches around Britain could soon go under.

STEEPLES

Rev. Randall believes several factors are responsible for the fall in attendances. "There's been a lack of investment" he told us. "Too much money has been spent on steeples, and not enough on the churches themselves. We're stuck with old, outdated buildings. Most of them lack even basic toilet facilities".

FORMAL

"Hymns are also outdated. Some of them are literally hundreds of years old. And I'm sure many young people are put off by the formal dress code. For instance, a church is probably the only place in Britain where you aren't allowed to wear a hat".

SHORTCOMING

Failure to compete in an increasingly competitive Sunday morning environment has been another major shortcoming, according to Rev. Randall. "DIY superstores and Garden Centres are pulling in the punters in their thousands, he told us.

Could churches like this soon be closing their doors for the last time. (Inset) Rev. Randall yesterday.

"They offer shopping, refreshments, play areas for the kids and free car parking. And all we have to offer is a cold seat, a couple of hymns and a few stories about God you've probably heard a hundred times before. It's no wonder we're losing out".

OUTSKIRTS

Among many suggestions he has put forward is the construction of new, out of town 'super-churches'. "The whole idea of the little church on the corner is completely outdated. We should be building big, new churches on the outskirts of town, with late opening, seven nights a week, and free car parking".

SPACE

Steps should also be taken to attract people to church. "Prime land is wasted on cemeteries. We could use this space to have attractive garden displays, fun fairs for kids, and car washes. Everyone washes their car on a Sunday".

FINAL

Rev. Randall believes a huge commercial opportunity exists in the form of Sunday lunches. "If we served up good, basic, traditional nosh, at reasonable prices, we'd have the punters queuing up for it", he told us.

'That's what churches need' says controversial vicar

The Reverend also dreams of the day when churches will be granted drinks licenses. "It's ridiculous", he told us. "You can buy a drink in any pub in the country. But if you're in a church you can't. Britain must be the only country in the world that has such outdated licensing laws. God only knows what tourists make of it all".

FRONTIER

Rev. Randall believes the key to future success will be attracting young people back to church. "We must try to get families back. It's all well and good the old folks turning up – they're always welcome – but a lot of them are only interested in the free cup of tea afterwards. And they're not exactly the most generous people in the world when the collection plate comes round".

BISHOP

So far Rev. Randall's suggestions have met with a cautious response from the Arch Bishop of Canterbury. "He hasn't actually replied yet", Rev. Randall admitted, "but he's been very busy lately".

ROOK

Meanwhile, the Reverend tells us that he hopes to attract a bumper congregation to his church on Christmas Day, by lining up a troup of exotic dancers to top the bill. "There's nothing in the Bible to say thou shalt not have strippers on", he joked yesterday. "And besides, anything that puts arses on pews is good business in my book". To overcome the drinks ban Rev. Randall will be inviting parishioners to bring along their own bottle of wine.

Trevor's poll tax shocker

Unemployed gas fitter Trevor Tomlinson, from Prestatyn, North Wales, almost fell through the floor when he opened his Community Charge bill from the local council.

FAN

For as well as Trevor's Poll Tax, the bill contained an additional charge of £24,000 – for a Pifco plastic oscillating fan which Trevor keeps on the top of the fridge in the kitchen.

HOT

"It's ludicrous", he told us yesterday. "I only ever use the fan once or twice a year when it gets really hot. How I'm supposed to afford £24,000 I'll never know.

"I've already had to sell my car, most of my furniture and re-mortgage the house, but I haven't raised half the cash yet. I wish I'd never seen the bloody fan. I wouldn't care. It only cost me £12. And it doesn't even work, because all the stuff has all come out of the batteries".

WELSH

We asked for a comment from a spokeman for Prestatyn council, but it was in Welsh.

Jack Black
& his dog Silver
in
The Mysterious Carol Singer ~

The Christmas holidays were here at last and young Jack Black and his dog, Silver, were staying with his Aunt Meg in her crofter's cottage in Northumberland.

It was Christmas Eve. Aunt Meg was baking a cake when suddenly, there was a knock at the door.

I WONDER WHO THAT CAN BE ON CHRISTMAS EVE?

GOSH, AUNT MEG, A CAROL SINGER.

GOD REST YE MERRY GENTLEMEN, LET NOTHING YOU DISMAY ...

... REMEMBER CHRIST OUR SAVIOUR WAS BORN ON CHRISTMAS DAY ...

All too soon, the old man had finished his song.

COR, THAT WAS SPLENDID . SING ANOTHER, PLEASE.

I'M SORRY, JACK, BUT I MUST BE ON MY WAY ...

... I WANT TO COLLECT AS MUCH MONEY FOR THE ORPHANAGE AS I CAN.

Aunt Meg made a generous donation.

HERE. I HOPE YOU AND THE ORPHANS HAVE A WONDERFUL CHRISTMAS.

GOD BLESS YOU, MEG.

Later that evening, Jack took Silver for a walk into the village.

COME ON SILVER, PUSH.

HNNNNNNN!

Suddenly, Jack noticed a light from the windows of Thompson's Toy Shop ...

THAT'S ODD ...

... WHY WOULD THE TOY SHOP BE OPEN AT THIS TIME OF NIGHT?

... he decided to investigate.

Through the window he saw a familiar face ...

GOSH! IT'S THE CAROL SINGER!

THERE'S THE TOYS FOR THE ORPHANS, GEORGE. THAT'LL BE FOUR POUNDS TEN AND SIX. I'VE THROWN IN A FEW EXTRA ONES FOR NOTHING.

THANKS VERY MUCH, TOM. I APPRECIATE THAT.

That night, Jack lay in bed, thinking.

Bless this

TOYS ... CAROL SINGING ... SOMETHING'S GOING ON ...

... AND I INTEND TO GET TO THE BOTTOM OF IT.

The next morning, Christmas Day, Jack was up bright and early, just like every other child.

JACK, AREN'T YOU GOING TO OPEN YOUR PRESENTS?

NOT NOW AUNT MEG, THERE'S IMPORTANT DETECTIVE WORK TO BE DONE.

COME ON, SILVER, WE'VE GOT WORK TO DO. THEN WE'VE GOT TO GO TO THE ORPHANAGE.

WOOF!

At the orphanage, Jack and Silver took up positions, hiding behind the wall.

Shortly, a man dressed as Santa Claus approached up the path.

AHA! JUST AS I THOUGHT.

The young orphans were delighted to see him and crowded round, squealing with excitement.

MERRY CHRISTMAS, CHILDREN. THERE'S TOYS FOR EVERYONE.

HOORAY!

Jack knew it was time to act ...

PHEEP!!

... and he gave a signal.

GPD-CD 10-90

On Jack's signal, two waiting policemen sped towards the Santa Claus in a fast car.

GPD-CD

EH? WHAT'S THIS?

HOLD IT RIGHT THERE.

WHAT'S GOING ON?

The policemen quickly seized and unmasked the villain.

JUST AS YOU SAID, JACK ...

... YES, THE CAROL SINGER.

BUT WHAT HAVE I DONE?

IT'S A GOOD JOB YOU CALLED US, JACK. NOT ONLY WAS HE COLLECTING MONEY FOR CHARITY WITHOUT A LICENCE, BUT HE ALSO PURCHASED THE ORPHANS' TOYS ON CHRISTMAS EVE, A SUNDAY.

YES. THAT'S A CLEAR BREACH OF THE TRADING LAWS.

COME ON. YOU AND YOUR ORPHAN COHORTS WILL BE SPENDING CHRISTMAS IN PRISON.

I'LL CALL FOR A VAN, SARGE.

WHAT ABOUT ALL THE TOYS, SERGEANT? WHAT'S GOING TO HAPPEN TO THEM?

HMMMM. I'VE GOT AN IDEA.

Later that day ...

WASN'T IT SUPER OF THE SERGEANT TO LET YOU KEEP ALL THE TOYS, JACK?

YES, I'M GOING TO HAVE A SPLENDID CHRISTMAS, AUNT MEG.

WOOF.

Lights! Camera! And red hot pumping
SEX ACTION!

Most people dream of having sex with their favourite film stars. But Burt Gubbins is lucky – he does it for a living! He's the world's highest paid *sex stuntman*, standing in for the stars to perform their steamy sex scenes. And here he reveals for the first time the scintillating secrets of a career spent *in bed* with some of the world's most glamorous film stars.

Bonking Bert's a box office blockbuster

Red hot sex scenes like this are all in a day's work for Bert.

YOU NAME 'EM I'VE BONKED 'EM

Fonda – dynamite

Agutter – shower

Kensit – fried eggs

❚❚ Every time you see a couple at it in a film you can bet your bottom dollar that it's me up there giving her one. And although you'll never see my face on the screen, you can be sure that I've got the *largest part* in the film!

Everyone knows the secret of a good movie is a red hot sex scene. But if the leading man can't cut the mustard, the whole movie could flop. And these days, despite their macho images, most of the top stars are a dead loss between the sheets. I've seen some of the biggest names in Tinseltown pull their pants down and not know what to do next.

KIT OFF

That's where I come in. I don't need a script or nothing, I just turn up, get my kit off and – *action!*

SEX

Sometimes they call me in if an actor is too shy to do the business. Like the time they were filming Klute. Donald Sutherland had refused to do a sex scene with Jane Fonda. Well, fuck me. I was in there like a shot!

CLAPPERS

Mind you, I've never had to work so hard in my life. The keep fit routine has certainly paid off for Jane Fonda. That bird is dynamite between the sheets! It was supposed to be a one minute love scene, but she had me going like the clappers for an hour and a half! In fact, we only stopped when the camera ran out of film.

POSITIONS

On another occasion I stood in for Donald filming Don't Look Back. Boy, that was another marathon session! I

Julie Christie yesterday.

had to knock off Julie Christie in that one. The director was a bit fussy, so he made us do it about fifty times, all in different positions. Mind you, I wasn't complaining! Eventually he was happy, and we sat down for a rest, only for the cameraman to tell us that the film hadn't

wound on. So we had to do it all over again!

In my line of work you never know what tomorrow will bring. One day I'll be shagging Emma Thomson on top of a piano in The Tall Guy, the next I'll be dressed up as a lion groping Bo Derek on the beach in Tarzan The Ape Man.

BLOW

One morning I got a phone call from David Lynch, the director. He said he was filming American Werewolf in London that afternoon, and could I come along and give Jenny Agutter a blow job in the shower. I didn't need asking twice!

TOOL

Under the British Film Censorship laws you aren't allowed to see my *tool of the trade* on screen. That can cause problems, as it's particularly difficult to hide, if you see what I mean. Anyway, subtle camera angles are used to get round

WOULD YOU LIKE ME TO LET YOUR TROUSERS OUT SIR?

WHINE! WHINE! SCRATCH! SCRATCH!

Rourke (left) was hell bent on bonking Bassinger (right).

'It would have taken Mickey 9½ weeks to get a bonk on'

the problem. For instance, that was my arse you saw going up and down in The Singing Detective.

SIZZLING

Naturally, a few actors still insist on doing their own sex. Mickey Rourke was determined to bonk Kim Bassinger himself in 9½ Weeks. There were some sizzling scenes in the script and Mickey was just dying to get stuck in. But when the cameras started to roll, he couldn't *stand up* to the pressure, and after half an hour they realised it wasn't just the focus that needed pulling.

PULL

They tried everything, without success. So eventually they had to *pull him off...* the set, that is. At the rate he was going it would have taken 9½ weeks just to get a bonk on. Needless to say, I was only too happy to oblige when they rang me up and asked me to stand in for Mickey.

GROPE

My *performances* have won me many fans among the stars. After I've warmed them up on set, a lot of them come after me begging for more. And a lot of them won't sign a movie contract unless they get a guarantee that I'm doing the sex scenes. Mind you, I've made that much dosh – getting millions of dollars for a quick grope and a bang – that I can afford to be choosy about parts myself now. These days I don't do a film unless I really fancy the bird.

For instance, I was asked to stand in for Mel Gibson in Lethal Weapon II, but I turned it down cos Patsy Kensit's got tits like fried eggs.

NOISES

One of my favourite jobs I get these days is dubbing new soundtracks on them arty films you get on Channel 4. They're just full of sex, and of course it's me they get to make the noises.

SHAG

I have to watch the film in a soundproof booth, wearing headphones. I have a great time in there, just me, a couple of birds to shag, and a few crates of beer.

STEAMY

People often ask me 'what's the best shag you've had with the stars?' And I reckon it has to be the one I had standing in for Jack Nicholson in The Postman Always Rings Twice. I'll never forget the steamy romp I had with Jessica Lange on the kitchen table! It took me ages to get the flour out of me pubes, I can tell you.

Northampton Says 'Cheese'

Northampton has been chosen as the venue for the 1994 National Cheese Festival.

The six month festival event, which will be jointly-financed by the European Development Agency, the Department of the Environment and Northampton Council Parks and Recreation Committee, will take place on a 500 acre site on the outskirts of the town, a derelict former shoe factory. The cost of converting the site into a spectacular venue for Britain's most extravagant cheese festival to date is estimated to be in the region of £250 billion.

CELEBRATION

Festival Director Mike Twatt believes the event will be good news for Northampton. "It will be a six month celebration of cheese, with cheese displays, exhibitions, and other things.

HIGHLIGHTS

Among the highlights will be the world's biggest piece of cheese. There will be cheese-orientated entertainment from around the world, cheese making demonstrations, a fun fair, refreshment facilities and car parking for 12 million cars in a specially-built car park at nearby Wellingborough".

PERM

"Not only will the festival bring jobs to Northampton – we are already advertising for car park attendants – it will also help attract new industry and investment, rejuvinating a former derelict eyesore, and making it into a hastily-assembled amusement park. We expect visitors to flood to Northampton in their thousands".

SHAMPOO & SET

Mr Twatt said he was relying on the people of Northampton and local industry to step in and make the event a success.

"If we can raise sufficient sponsorship from local firms, and if 120 million people visit the site, four times each, during the six-month period, the Festival will actually break even". Thirty-nine people visited the 1990 National Cheese Festival at Wolverhampton earlier this year.

IT'S BOLLOCKS

The word 'Bollocks' has been chosen as the British entry in next year's Eurovision Swear Contest, due to take place in Copenhagen in the Spring. Nations will be competing for first prize in the competition to find Europe's premier obscenity.

DUTCH

Among the contenders will be the Dutch entry 'Debiele', the French contender 'Putain' and the Greek profanity 'Skatta Nafas'.

TOWEL

This year will see the first entry from a united Germany since the competition began in 1952. The German contender 'Binden', literally translated, means sanitary towel.

LILLETS

Britain's entry will be performed by Felicity Kendall who will be hoping to improve on last year's dismal performance when Gareth Hunt came last with a dreadful rendition of the word 'toss'.

DEATH BED JOKE

AND HOW ARE YOU COPING?

OH, THE FAMILY ARE MARVELLOUS, THEY'RE ALL RALLYING ROUND.

VROOM!

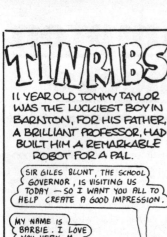

TINRIBS

11 YEAR OLD TOMMY TAYLOR WAS THE LUCKIEST BOY IN BARNTON, FOR HIS FATHER, A BRILLIANT PROFESSOR, HAD BUILT HIM A REMARKABLE ROBOT FOR A PAL.

COME ON PALS, LET'S HAVE A GAME OF FOOTER BEFORE THE FIRST LESSON.

BAH! THE HEAD HAS ORDERED ME TO POLISH ALL OBJECTS WHICH BEGIN WITH THE LETTER 'C' IN THE STAFFROOM IN PREPARATION FOR THE GOVERNOR'S VISIT!

'GUTBUCKET' SNODWORTHY

STAFF ROOM WINDOW

NICE SAVE, TINRIBS!

CLONK!

SIR GILES BLUNT, THE SCHOOL GOVERNOR, IS VISITING US TODAY — SO I WANT YOU ALL TO HELP CREATE A GOOD IMPRESSION.

MY NAME IS BARBIE. I LOVE YOU VERY M—

SHH, TINRIBS!

THAT'S THE CLOCK DONE — NOW FOR THE CHAIRS.

SMASH!

OOF!

WHAT IS THE MEANING OF THIS, SNODWORTHY? I WILL NOT HAVE MASTERS GOING AROUND WITH PIECES OF BROKEN GLASS PROTRUDING FROM THEIR FACES!

GROAN..OOER! THE HEAD!

..AND WHEN YOU'VE TIDIED YOURSELF UP, YOU CAN SET TO WORK LINING UP THE FURNITURE IN MY STUDY IN ALPHABETICAL ORDER. I WANT EVERYTHING TO BE JUST RIGHT FOR THE GOVERNOR.

YES HEADMASTER.

THAT MECHANICAL MENACE LANDED ME IN TROUBLE — SO I'M CONFISCATING YOUR FOOTBALL!

SPOILSPORT!

NEVER MIND. WE CAN PLAY AT THROWING THE JAVELIN INSTEAD — USING TINRIBS' ARM-PIECE AS A JAVELIN!

MY NAME IS BARBIE — I LOVE YOU VERY MUCH

GOSH! WHAT A THROW!

..AND AS YOU CAN SEE, SIR GILES, THE BICYCLES WITH FRAMES OF 27" OR MORE HAVE BEEN MARKED WITH AN 'X', WHILST THOSE WHICH ARE SMALLER HAVE BEEN...

HMM, YES

SUDDENLY—

URK!

THUNK!

GOOD LORD! SIR GILES' CHEST HAS BEEN PIERCED BY THIS PECULIAR STICK — WITHOUT IMMEDIATE SURGERY, HE WILL SURELY DIE!

GASP

SIR! THE JAGGED TOP OF THIS RUSTY OLD SOUP TIN, BORROWED FROM TINRIBS' VERTICAL SUPPORT, COULD SERVE AS AN IMPROVISED SCALPEL!

AND I'M THE BIOLOGY TEACHER SO I KNOW A BIT ABOUT MAJOR SURGERY!

CHOKE

I THINK

AND SO...

SHORTLY—

WELL DONE, TAYLOR. YOU AND YOUR ELECTRONIC CHUM HAVE BEEN A GREAT HELP — UNLIKE MR SNODWORTHY...

MUTTER

WHAT IS YOUR NAME? WILL YOU BE MY FRIEND?

CAH! THAT TIN TWERP IS NOTHING BUT TROUBLE!

SO I'LL GIVE YOU THIS FIVER IF YOU SORT OUT TAYLOR AND THAT HEAP OF AUTOMATED JUNK HE CALLS HIS PAL, ONCE AND FOR ALL!

SNEAKY SIMPSON

I'LL BUILD MY OWN ROBOTIC COMPANION — ONE WHICH WILL POUND THAT SOPPY TIN-BRAINED NIT INTO SCRAP!

..A LITTLE DROP OF THIS.. AND A LITTLE DROP OF THAT.. HA-AHAA-AHAAA!

AHAA-AH-HAA!

LATER

MR SNODWORTHY, I'D LIKE YOU TO MEET — CHROMESIDES!

HMM. IT LOOKS RATHER LIKE A CONCRETE PAVING SLAB WITH EMPTY EGG BOXES SELLOTAPED TO IT

TAP!

AND WHY HAVE YOU COATED IT WITH FOUL-SMELLING CHEMICALS?

GAAAHH!

TOPPLE

CRUNCH!

I'LL GIVE YOU ONE LAST CHANCE, SIMPKINS. DEAL WITH TAYLOR AND TINRIBS — OR I'LL DEAL WITH YOU!

OO-ER

A FEW ADJUSTMENTS WILL PUT PAID TO THIS METALLIC MORON

FIRST, I EXCHANGE THE VOICEBOX FOR A RECORDED TAPE I MADE EARLIER...

..THEN I REPLACE THIS REAR WHEEL WITH ONE I PROCURED FROM A SUPERMARKET TROLLEY

HEH-HEH. THIS SHOULD CAUSE A BIT OF A FRACAS!

SHOVE!

:CLICK:

ARSEHOLES!

WHAT TH-

FRIG!

NIPPLES!

BEARDED CLAM!

SWERVE

OH NO! TINRIBS HAS GONE BESERK!

..WHEREAS THE ROOT VEGETABLES HAVE BEEN NAILED TO THE...

RINGPIECE!

CHEESEY HELMET FLAKES!

I'VE NEVER BEEN SO INSULTED IN MY LIFE! I SHALL RECOMMEND THAT THE SCHOOL BE RAZED TO THE GROUND IMMEDIATELY, AND HAVE A NEW SHOPPING COMPLEX BUILT IN IT'S PLACE!

B-BUT SIR GILES...

GOOD DAY HEADMASTER.

GRR! RIGHT! IT'S A SEVERE WHACKING FOR WHOEVER IS RESPONSIBLE FOR THIS OUTRAGE!

HOWEVER, I AM A FAIR MAN, AND HAVE NO WISH TO SHOW BIAS AGAINST ANY PARTICULAR INDIVIDUAL.

THEREFORE, MISS PEASON WILL BLINDFOLD ME, AND WHOEVER I 'TAG' SHALL BE HELD CULPABLE.

TAG!

ERK!

AHA! SO, SIMPKINS! YOU'RE THE CULPRIT!

GULP!

MR SNODWORTHY WILL ALSO RECEIVE A BEATING, BECAUSE HE IS FAT. SO THE REST OF YOU MIGHT AS WELL TAKE THE DAY OFF.

!

HURRAH FOR TOMMY AND HIS EXTRAORDINARY 'MILESTONE OF RESEARCH INTO THE DEVELOPMENT OF ARTIFICIAL INTELLIGENCE' SOULMATE!

WHACK WHACK

FROTTAGE!

LetterBocks

LetterBocks LetterBocks LetterBocks LetterBocks Lette

From the top of your head to the tip of your socks
It's your favourite page, it's Letterbox!

Rich man's heaven problem

LETTERBOCKS
VIZ COMIC
P.O. BOX 1PT
NEWCASTLE-UPON-TYNE
NE99 1PT

According to the Bible, it is easier for a camel to pass through the eye of a needle than it is for a rich man to enter the Kingdom of Heaven.
Well, that's Cliff Richard fucked then.

Mr I. Lancer
Croydon

Yesterday was our wedding anniversary and over breakfast I told my wife I loved her. "I love you too", I heard her reply.
Imagine my surprise when she left me this morning to go and live with several members of the pretentious and untalented Irish rock band U2.
Do I win £5?

H. Chaparal
Luton

Biscuits please

I am collecting the foil wrappers from Viscount biscuits, Yo-yos and Tunnock's teacakes for Romania. I have already sent them two large envelopes full. My sister, who is 87, is collecting the foil bits from Kit Kats and Bar Sixes.
If any of your readers have any Viscount biscuits, Yo-yos, Tunnock's teacakes, Kit Kats or Bar Sixes perhaps they could send the wrappers to me. Please could you clean them first, and flatten them with a spoon.
I will send the Kit Kat and Bar Six wrappers to my sister. Please, if you are sending Kit Kat or Bar Six wrappers, please also send £1.20 for additional postage as my sister lives in Canada where unfortunately they do not have Kit Kats or Bar Sixes.
I am 98 years of age.

Miss Irene Porterhouse
Address withheld by request

*Letterbox is **YOUR** chance to have your say. If you've got a strong opinion on a topical issue, and feel that you have got something worth saying, then drop us a line. There's a very slim chance indeed that we'll print your letter.*
In each issue we claim to award a special prize to the sender of the best letter. So grab those pens and pencils and get writing. You could be our next lucky winner!

God let me down

Who says God exists and is all powerful? The other day I prayed for twenty minutes for him to fix the gearbox on my Austin 1800. And did he? Did he arse!
If anything he's made it worse. I can't even get it into first gear now.

J. Dury
Huddersfield

When he refers to God (Letterbox, Viz 46), Mr Dury fails to understand the ways of our Lord. Of course God exists. He speaks to me every night, and tells me to kill women. I have already killed four, and he rewards me with coloured lights and music in my head.

Mr D. McLure
Salford

The kind of prices which are bandied about in the Antiques Roadshow are a load of nonsense. I took an old chair of mine along to an antique shop and was told it was only worth twenty quid.

P. Duel
Sevenoaks

I hardly think it's fair that poll tax dodgers who refuse to pay the Community Charge should benefit from council services towards which they do not contribute.
I suggest council binmen be put under strict orders not to empty the bins of anyone who fails to pay their poll tax.

B. Murphy
Stocksfield

Highway to heaven

I have an experience I would like to share with your readers.
Last Sunday, whilst watching Harry Secombe's 'Highway' programme on TV, I was suddenly filled with the love of God. It came upon me suddenly, like a bright light from Heaven, and all at once I was filled with joy as Jesus came unto me and entered my life.
Fortunately it went away during the commercial break and I was back to normal again.

B. O. Nanza
Burton-on-Trent

I look forward to celebriti dying, because then we g to see all their best films TV.
I hope Clint Eastwood di next. I think he's great.

Mrs F. J. Sommavill
Norwic

I believe police shou be given photographs people who have not pay their poll tax, and if the see them being mugged the street, they should tu a blind eye.

B. Murph
Stocksfiel

No new is good news

They say 'no news is goo news'. Well, my grandfath er went on a two wee camping holiday in Zambi in 1942 and hasn't been see since. So I hardly think th saying applies in this case.

C. Woestman
Hollywoo

A large yellow cross shoul be painted on the door anyone who refuses to pa their poll tax so that if th property catches fire, th fire brigade will know no to put it out.

B. Murph
Stocksfiel

I am nipping out for a quick pint in ten minutes and wondered whether any o your readers would care t join me.

S. Shoreham
Sheffiel

LetterBocks LetterBocks LetterBocks LetterBocks LetterBocks Letter

SCORE
DOCTOR 34
PATIENT 0

DOCTOR. I'M GOING TO POT. I NEED A BREAK.

YOU OUGHT TO HAVE A LONG REST.

Bocks Letter LetterBocks LetterB cks

top Tips

DON'T throw away those old balloons after Christmas. Stretched over your head they make ideal shower caps.
Mrs D. Topping
Derby

AMUSE family and friends by placing an old plant pot on your head and doing a comedy impression of Tommy Cooper. Just like that!
R. Alderson
Nantwich

MAKE your neighbour think you are an alien by wrapping yourself in tin foil and standing in your garden late at night pointing at the stars and making silly, high pitched 'bleeping' noises.
Mr B. Mirellees
March

DON'T risk drowning if you travel by boat. Simply put on a pair of bicycle clips and fill your trousers with ping-pong balls.
A. Clayton
Glasgow

SAVE money at Christmas by not sending cards or presents to elderly relatives who's marbles have probably gone anyway and who wouldn't know you from Adam.
B. Peacock
Swindon

VARNISH digestive biscuits to make attractive but slightly brittle drink coasters.
B. Thompson
Houston

PAINT a series of dots onto Bourbon biscuits, then varnish them. Hey presto! Dominoes.
B. Thompson
Houston

DIVIDE your lawn into a grid using string and wooden pegs. You can then describe your exact postion in the garden over the telephone to a friend or relative many miles away who would then be able to plot your movements on a piece of graph paper.
R. H. Lorimer
Peebles

STRIKE a match at football games every time a goal is scored. When the game ends simply count the number of used matches to reveal the final score.
Mr U. Biscuits
Rotherham

CARRY a different vegetable in your pocket each weekday to remind you which day it is. For example Sunday — a sprout, Monday — a marrow, Tuesday — a turnip, Wednesday. . . Etc.
I. Tobacco
Bradford

FROZEN SPROUTS make a tasty alternative to boiled sweets, and they don't rot kids teeth.
Mrs F. Penn
Burnley

GET into the cinema free by looking bored, carrying an ice cream tray and wearing a silly hat.
Mrs D. Table
Hendon

Les is no lezza!

SHOWBIZ colleagues have leapt to the defence of Family Fortunes star Les Dennis, scotching rumours about his sex life before they have even started.

LES

"Les is no lesbian", one showbiz insider blasted. "He is happily married, and would never get involved in that sort of thing."

LYNNE

A source close to the 36-year-old star yesterday confirmed that Dennis and his pretty wife Lynne were perfectly happy together.

Dennis, 36, was last night believed to staying with friends.

YOU BLOODY TRAITOR!

Britain's wartime Prime Minister Winston Churchill came within a whisker of SURRENDERING to Germany during the early stages of the war, according to top secret government papers only recently made available to the public.

And the highly sensitive documents, kept under lock and key for the last 50-years, reveal that Britain's wartime hero planned to strike a deal with Nazi boss Adolf Hitler.

BALLOON

Minutes of a wartime cabinet meeting reveal how in 1940 Churchill planned to betray his country and fly to Berlin in a hot-air balloon, taking with him the Crown Jewels as a peace offering to the Nazi dictator. He was to be accompanied on his traitorous journey by his long-time mistress, forties pop singer Gracie Fields.

STREAMER

Churchill and Fields planned to live together in Berlin under an assumed name. But their plot was foiled when Fields panicked at the eleventh hour and jumped twenty feet from the balloon as it took off from Churchill's allotment in Surrey. Fields suffered a sprained ankle in the fall.

DESPERATE

The desperate Prime Minister's daring balloon bid ended shortly afterwards when he was shot down by a member of the Surbiton Home Guard.

Churchill planned to strike deal with Nazis

Churchill – balloon bid

Top doctors who examined Churchill afterwards found that he was suffering from stress, and after he personally apologised to the Queen for his actions he was allowed to carry on as Prime Minister. For if news of his surrender mission had become public, untold damage would have been done to Britain's wartime moral.

DAN

Churchill died in 1965, and his funeral was on telly.

Herman's Hermit

YOUNG HERMAN HOBSON WAS THE LUCKIEST BOY IN BARNTON, FOR HE HAD A SPECIAL PAL - A HERMIT WHO LIVED AT THE BOTTOM OF THE GARDEN.

HI, READERS! I'M OFF TO HAVE AN ADVENTURE WITH MY HERMIT CHUM!

SO... HEY, HERMIT! ARE YOU COMING OUT TO HAVE AN ADVENTURE?

FUCK OFF... ...LEAVE ME ALONE

MORE RECLUSIVE HILARITY NEXT TIME!

THE ADVENTURES OF ROLF HARRIS THE CAT

VICE VICAR'S NIGHT OF SIN

A practicing vicar made love to a naked woman in a vicarage only yards from his church.

Then the saucy cleric got up, put his clothes on and **STROLLED** into church only hours later, to preach **RELIGION** to his congregation.

SEX

Innocent churchgoers at the quiet Kent village of Borpington had no idea their vicar had been **HAVING SEX** only hours before, or that the blond beauty he had frolicked with was none other than his **WIFE**.

INTERCOURSE

Vicar Fletcher Plywood's X certificate antics were exposed only after his attractive wife Vera became pregnant. Plywood, 33, does not deny that **FULL SEX** took place. Meanwhile villagers in Borpington were too shocked to comment.

"It's a disgrace to think that his has been going on under our noses", said one yesterday.

FLASHED

A spokesman for the Church of England yesterday flashed a **GREEN LIGHT** to lusty vicars. He told us that vicars were **ALLOWED** to have sex with their wives, and that many had families as a result.

According to church officials only left footed vicars – or 'priests' – face a bonking ban.

EXCLUSIVE

Randy Rev 'had sex in vicarage'

What do YOU think?

Do you think it's right that Church of England vicars should be allowed to have sex left, right and centre, while their catholic counterparts can only sit and watch? Surely **ALL** men of God should face a ban on bonking, unless the churches introduce a sex free-for-all, with Holy men of all denominations able to join in.

We want to know what **YOU** think on the issue of vicar sex. Fill in the voting slip below, and we'll publish the results of our survey in the next issue. Probably.

To: Viz Vicar Sex Debate, P.O. Box 1PT, Newcastle upon Tyne, NE99 1PT.

I think that*
- [ ] **ALL VICARS**
- [ ] **NO VICARS**
- [ ] **ONLY RIGHT FOOTED VICARS**

should be allowed to have sex.

*Tick one box only.   Signed_____

It's 'Bus' Abbot

Neighbours of madcap TV clown Russ Abbott are being driven round the bend.

For the crazy king of comedy has gone bananas about buses – amassing a collection of 116 double deckers in the garden of his £1 million house in Cheadle Hume, Essex.

"He's bus bonkers", one neighbour told us. "I knew he was nuts just from watching his crazy TV show, but now he's gone double decker dotty! We're 'all a-bored' with it".

ZANY

Lesbian slur star Les Dennis confirmed that his zany colleague Abbott was a busaholic. "I know his garden is piled high with the things, but I'm sure Russ will find room for *one more on top*", quipped Dennis.

Billy the Fish

BILLY THOMSON, TOGETHER WITH THE ENTIRE STAFF OF FULCHESTER UNITED FOOTBALL CLUB, HAS BEEN ARRESTED FOR TAX EVASION. ALSO, THE CLUB HAS BEEN RELEGATED TO DIVISION 8 OF THE OVALTINE DEVON AND CORNWALL AREA SUNDAY LEAGUE...

I DON'T UNDERSTAND. I'VE NEVER SEEN ANY OF THIS MONEY BEFORE IN MY LIFE!

I DON'T WANT TO GO TO PRISON TOMMY.

DON'T WORRY SYD. WE'RE INNOCENT. WE'VE GOT NOTHING TO FEAR.

COME ALONG. THERE'S A PRISON VAN WAITING FOR YOU LOT.

!?

OH NO! I DON'T BELIEVE IT! IT'S TV PRANKSTER JEREMY BEADLE!

YES. WE CERTAINLY FOOLED YOU THERE EH TOMMY? AND IT WAS YOUR COACH SYD PRESTON WHO SET YOU UP!

BAH! I'LL GET YOU FOR THIS SYD! HO HO!

HA HA HA!

THE NEXT DAY, FULCHESTER FACE A BOXING DAY DERBY WITH LOCAL RIVALS FULCHESTER CITY.

AS THE TEAMS WARM UP...

WHAT DID YOU DO LAST NIGHT BILLY?

I WENT TO SEE THAT NEW FILM WITH PATRICK SWAYZE.

OH YEAH - "GHOST". WHAT'S IT LIKE?

IT'S REALLY SAD. ESPECIALLY THE ENDING.

IN FACT, JUST THINKING ABOUT IT BRINGS A TEAR TO MY EYE.

HEY LOOK! BILLY THOMSON'S CRYING!

FRANKLY I'M CHOKED FOR THE LAD.

GASP!

YES.

BOO HOO!

SNIFF!

PSSST! HEY BILLY! KEEP UP THE TEARS SON.

?

I'M TOP PROMOTER AND AGENT FRANK McSPORRAN, AND IF YOU KEEP CRYING, I'LL MAKE YOU A MILLIONAIRE!

THE NEXT DAY...

BILLY WEEPS IN BOXING DAY DERBY! READ ALL ABOUT IT!

IT'S BILLY MANIA!

BILLY TO MAKE RECORD!!

TEARS OF A FISH!

THE NEXT DAY BILLY IS SET TO APPEAR ON THE TERRY WIGGON SHOW...

ERM... I THINK YOU'VE HAD ENOUGH TO DRINK NOW, BILLY. DON'T FORGET TO PLUG YOUR NEW RECORD, THE BOOK, THE PERFUME, THE SHOES...

...THE KITCHEN UTENSILS, THE SAVOURY BISCUITS, THE SWIMSUITS ETC...

OKAY... HIC!

SO... LADIES & GENTLEMEN... WILL YOU PLEASE GIVE A BIG WELCOME TO THE MOST POPULAR FOOTBALLING FISH IN THE COUNTRY... BILLY THOMSON!

HOORAY! HOORAY!

WELCOME TO THE SHOW BILLY.

HELLO THERE TERRY... HIC!!

WELL BILLY, YOU'VE CERTAINLY HIT THE HEADLINES IN THE LAST COUPLE OF DAYS.

AAAH FUCK OFF YOU WIGGY FAT BASTARD... HIC!

I LIKE SHAGGING! HIC!

BAT!

IT'S SO EMBARRASSING SYD. I CAN'T BEAR TO WATCH.

YES. IT'S PATHETIC. HE'S LET HIMSELF DOWN.

AFTER THE SHOW... YOU'RE A DISGRACE BILLY. YOU'RE FINISHED. I'M TEARING UP YOUR CONTRACT. AND I'M KEEPING ALL YOUR MONEY.

YOU CAN'T DO THAT! I'LL KILL YOU FIRST! I'LL SHOOT YOU WITH A GUN!

LATER, AS McSPORRAN LEAVES THE STUDIOS, A SHADOWY FIGURE APPROACHES...

FTV STUDIOS

AAAARGH!

BANG!

THE NEXT DAY... SHADOWY FIGURE IN BALACLAVA HELMET GUNS DOWN TOP PROMOTER!

FRANK McSPORRAN SHOT!

READ ALL ABOUT IT!

MEANWHILE... BILLY "THE FISH" THOMSON. I'M ARRESTING YOU FOR THE ATTEMPTED MURDER OF TOP PROMOTER FRANK McSPORRAN.

B-BUT... BUT... I WAS AT MY AUNTIE'S HOUSE...

DID BILLY SHOOT FRANK McSPORRAN? WILL HE GO TO PRISON FOR ATTEMPTED MURDER? DON'T MISS THE NEXT EPISODE!!!

Aldridge Prior

The HOPELESS LIAR

NOT ME

NO

BEWARE OF THE LIONS

AND THE CROCODILES

16

DING! DONG!

THERE'S NOBODY IN. WELL, EXCEPT ME, AND I'M OUT... I WENT OUT ABOUT TWENTY MINUTES AGO. ...NO, TWO HOURS.

35

I'M FROM THE POLL TAX OFFICE. I'D LIKE TO SPEAK TO... THE NOLAN SISTERS.

I AM THE NOLAN SISTERS.

AH, MR. PRIOR, I'D LIKE TO ASK A FEW QUESTIONS ABOUT DISCREPENCIES ARISING FROM A POLL TAX FORM YOU FILLED IN.

NOW IT SAYS THERE ARE SEVENTEEN PERSONS LIVING AT THIS ADDRESS; A MISS CLODAH ROGERS, BRITT EKLAND, SABRINA PANS PEOPLE, DEBBIE GIBSON, THE LEAD SINGER OUT OF THE BANGLES, CHERI LUNGI, ...I COULD GO ON.

YES, THAT'S RIGHT.

I CAN'T HELP BUT NOTICE THAT OUR RECORDS SHOW THIS PROPERTY TO BE A ONE BEDROOM FLAT. IS THIS NOT THE CASE MR. PRIOR?

ERM, YES, EVERYONE'S BEEN SLEEPING ON THE SETTEE... EXCEPT THE NOLANS. THE NOLANS ALL SLEEP WITH ME YOU SEE.

WOULD IT BE POSSIBLE FOR ME TO SPEAK TO THE NOLAN SISTERS?

OH, ERM, YOU'VE JUST MISSED THEM. THEY'VE GONE SHOPPING... TO BUY SOME TROUSER SUITS.

COULD I COME INSIDE PLEASE?

ERM...NO. THERE'S A SWARM OF KILLER BEES IN THE KITCHEN, YOU WOULD BE STUNG.

INSIDE... I DON'T SEE ANY BEES MR. PRIOR.

NO, NO, THEY'VE HIDDEN UNDER THE COOKER YOU SEE... INGENIOUS.

ACTUALLY THE RABBIT'S EATEN THEM ALL.

I WAS WONDERING... COULD YOU POSSIBLY SHOW ME WHERE, FOR INSTANCE, FELICITY KENDALL SLEEPS?

JUST HERE... IN THIS CUPBOARD... BY THE GAS METER IN FACT... OF COURSE SHE TAKES ALL THESE PANS OUT FIRST.

CAN I GET YOU SOME TEA? I HAVE ALMOST TWO THOUSAND BLENDS TO CHOOSE FROM.

OH LOVELY, AMONGST THAT LOT YOU MUST HAVE MY FAVOURITE – DARJEELING.

OH, OF COURSE I DON'T HAVE ANY TEA – CAN'T STAND THE STUFF. HOW ABOUT REAL COFFEE? – EIGHT HUNDRED DIFFERENT ROASTS.

OH...ERM...YES, ANYTHING THAT'S CONVENIENT.

I'M AFRAID A TRAINED MONKEY FROM THE CIRCUS HAS STOLEN MY KETTLE, THAT'S THE FIFTEENTH ONE I'VE LOST IN AS MANY DAYS.

YES, NOW MR. PRIOR, DO YOU REALISE THAT THE INFORMATION YOU HAVE GIVEN ON THIS FORM IS LEGALLY BINDING AND WILL BE USED TO ASSESS YOUR POLL-TAX?

OF COURSE I DO. I WAS THE CHANCELLOR OF THE EXCHEQUOR IN THE LATE FIFTIES.

CAN YOU CONFIRM THAT THIS IS YOUR SOLE RESIDENCE IN THE U.K.?

YES. APART FROM THE CASTLE IN SCOTLAND. ...BOTH THE CASTLES IN SCOTLAND.

TWO CASTLES IN SCOTLAND THEN EH?

YES. THREE ACTUALLY. AND A FARM IN WALES. TWO FARMS... AND OF COURSE THE FOUR CASTLES. NOT INCLUDING THE OTHER FARM AND CASTLE.

I SEE... VERY INTERESTING. WELL MR. PRIOR, ON THE BASIS OF THE INFORMATION YOU HAVE GIVEN ME I HAVE ASSESSED YOUR POLL-TAX BILL AS FOLLOWS...

TAP! TAP!

TAP! TAP!

FOR SEVENTEEN PERSONS AT THIS ADDRESS YOU OWE £8,330, AND FOR YOUR EIGHT OTHER RESIDENCES IN SCOTLAND AND WALES £7,840 IS OUTSTANDING.

HERE YOU GO, YOUR POLL-TAX BILL FOR £16,170.

CHEERS. I'LL RUN UP A CHEQUE FROM ONE OF MY SWISS BANK ACCOUNTS THIS AFTERNOON. I HAVE A FINE ART COLLECTION WORTH EIGHT HUNDRED MILLION YOU KNOW... TWICE THAT MUCH IN FACT.

A. PRIOR YOU OWE HER MAJESTY'S GOVERNMENT £16,170 PAY UP YOU PEASANT

SEVERAL MONTHS LATER...

MR. PRIOR, YOU HAVE BEEN FOUND GUILTY OF NON-PAYMENT OF POLL-TAX, DO YOU HAVE ANYTHING TO SAY BEFORE I PASS LUDICROUS AND UNFAIR SENTENCE UPON YOU?

YES, YOUR HONOUR.

YOU'VE GOT THE WRONG MAN.

MY NAME IS DAVID ICKE.

I GAVE UP A FINE CAREER AS A SPORTS PRESENTER IN ORDER TO DEVOTE MY TIME AND ENERGY TO THE ENVIRONMENTAL ISSUES WHICH AFFECT OUR PLANET'S FUTURE...

...AND YOU CAN'T PUT ME IN PRISON ANYWAY... BECAUSE I'M PREGNANT... WITH TWINS.

Kid Politician

YOUNG NEVILLE FROTTER HAD ALWAYS ONLY ONE AMBITION IN LIFE— TO BECOME A MEMBER OF PARLIAMENT!

ONE MORNING...
GOOD MORNING, NEVILLE

SIT AT THE TABLE FOR YOUR BREAKFAST

AH, HELLO, MRS. FROTTER. HOW LOVELY TO SEE YOU. HOW LONG HAVE YOU BEEN A HOUSEWIFE? REALLY, THAT'S VERY INTERESTING...

I'M SURE I CAN COUNT ON YOUR SUPPORT...GOODBYE

...HELLO...ER... MISTER FROTTER. IT'S VERY NICE TO MEET YOU...
NEVER MIND THAT, YOUNG MAN. HAVE YOU CLEANED YOUR BEDROOM UP? IT'S A RIGHT MESS
ER...YYYYES...

...LOOK, MR. FROTTER, I SHARE YOUR CONCERNS ABOUT THE STATE OF THE ROOM, AND I INTEND TO DO MY BEST TO LOOK INTO THE MATTER ON YOUR BEHALF...
BUT NOW, I'M AFRAID I HAVE PRESSING MATTERS

SHORTLY...
OH, ISN'T SHE A LOVELY LITTLE GIRL. YOU MUST BE VERY PROUD
HE'S A BOY

REALLY? HOW OLD IS SHE?
GOODBYE

AT THE SCHOOL GATES...
FROTTER! YOU'RE LATE AGAIN
NO! NO, I DON'T THINK I AM..

...AND I THINK THE STATISTICS WILL BEAR ME OUT HERE, THAT I HAVE, IN FACT, SHOWN A MARKED DECREASE IN LATENESS AFTER SEASONAL ADJUSTMENTS, OVER THE LAST SEVEN DAYS...
...NOT INCLUDING TODAY, WEDNESDAY AND PERHAPS MONDAY
I THINK THOSE FIGURES SPEAK FOR THEMSELVES!

NOW LISTEN HERE, FROTTER...
...NO, LET ME FINISH, YOU ASKED A QUESTION, NOW LET ME ANSWER...
YOU'LL GET YOUR TURN LATER

IT'S ALL VERY WELL TO LOOK AT THE SUPERFICIAL PROBLEMS OF LATENESS, BUT I THINK WE SHOULD LOOK AT THE UNDER ISSUES

I BLAME A LACK OF INVESTMENT COUPLED WITH THE MISMANAGEMENT OF EXISTING RESOURCES BY PREVIOUS GOVERNMENTS, AND I THINK IF WE'RE EVER TO GET THE FIGURES DOWN TO AN ACCEPTABLE LEVEL WITHIN THE RECOMMENDATIONS OF MY PINK PAPER, WE ALL HAVE TO TIGHTEN OUR BELTS

IN CLASS
AH! FROTTER, AT LAST! NOW, HAVE YOU DONE YOUR HOMEWORK?

WELL, I'D LIKE TO ANSWER THAT QUESTION IN TWO WAYS IF I MAY. FIRSTLY, I DON'T THINK THAT HOMEWORK IS THE KEY ISSUE HERE. IT WOULD BE VERY SHORT SIGHTED OF US TO.....

TONK

HAVE YOU DONE YOUR HOMEWORK, BOY?
NO, SIR!

RIGHT, GO AND REPORT TO THE HEADMASTER, IMMEDIATELY. I'VE HAD ENOUGH OF YOU!
OUCH! IT'S NOT FAIR! IT'S NOT RIGHT! IT'S NOT ETHICAL!

SO...
HEAD
KNOCK KNOCK
COME IN!

INSIDE...
YOU AGAIN, FROTTER! THIS IS THE FOURTH TIME THIS WEEK YOU'VE BEEN SENT TO SEE ME!
YES! BUT IT'S ONLY THE THIRD TIME IN REAL TERMS, SIR!

NOW, I'VE BEEN LOOKING AT YOUR RECORDS, FROTTER. IT SEEMS YOU'RE A BRASH, ARROGANT, SELF OPINIONATED, UNREASONABLE, SELFISH SMARMY YOUNG MAN...

...I'M GOING TO MAKE YOU HEAD BOY
OOH! THAT'S VERY DECENT OF YOU, MR. PROCTOR

NOW, IN TRUE BLUE STYLE, I'M GOING TO GIVE YOU A JOLLY GOOD SPANKING. BEND OVER, BOY.
OOH, YES PLEASE, SIR!

GPD. CD. ST. 6.90
VIZ 4-3

66

MAXWELL STRAKER Record Breaker!

IF YOU WANT TO BE THE BEST IF YOU WANT TO BEAT THE REST WUH-OH-OH-DEDICATION'S WHAT YOU NEED!

BLOOO-AARGH!!

HAVE YOU BEEN EATING LARD AGAIN MAXWELL?

YES I HAVE.

BUT IF I'M EVER TO BEAT JON BROWER MINNOCH'S 1978 WORLD RECORD FOR BEING FAT WHEN HE WEIGHED 99 STONE ONE POUND...

I'M GOING TO HAVE TO INCREASE MY CALORIFIC INTAKE QUITE DRAMATICALLY.

DON'T TALK SO DAFT. YOU'RE GOING TO BE LATE FOR SCHOOL.

OOYAH!

BAH. I'LL NEVER GET IN THE BOOK AT THIS RATE.

AT SCHOOL...

SIR! SIR! DID YOU KNOW THAT MRS. SHAKUNTALA DEVI OF INDIA MULTIPLIED TWO 13-DIGIT NUMBERS TOGETHER IN HER HEAD IN TWENTY-EIGHT SECONDS?

IT'S A RECORD I INTEND TO SMASH HERE THIS AFTERNOON!

WOULD YOU PLEASE SELECT, AT RANDOM, TWO 13-DIGIT NUMBERS, AND WRITE THEM ON THE BLACKBOARD.

START THE STOPWATCH!

7106321549236 × 2104613978192

TWO TIMES SIX IS TWELVE... ER TWO DOWN... CARRY ONE...

LATER THAT NIGHT...

...THREE'S THREE IS NINE, PLUS TWELVE IS TWENTY... NO... YES... CARRY TWO... ER... OH DEAR... RIGHT. TWO TIMES SIX IS TWELVE...

NEXT DAY...

ON THE 2nd JANUARY, 1988, DUTCH STUDENTS TOPPLED 1,382,101 DOMINOES WITH A SINGLE PUSH.

THAT RECORD WON'T TAKE MUCH BEATING.

HALF AN HOUR LATER...

BAH. I'VE RAN OUT OF DOMINOES!

THERE'S ONLY 28 IN THE BOX.

LATER...

HALF TO DOVER PLEASE.

THE CHANNEL SWIMMING RECORD IS PRESENTLY HELD BY PENNY DEAN - AND STANDS AT 7 HOURS 40 MINUTES.

OH CRUMBS. I FORGOT. I CAN'T SWIM.

HALF TO FULCHESTER PLEASE.

ONE OF THE ZANIEST FEATS IN THE BOOK IS SMASHING AN UPRIGHT PIANO, AND PASSING THE WRECKAGE THROUGH A NINE INCH CIRCLE.

ONE MINUTE, THIRTY-SEVEN SECONDS IS THE WORLD RECORD.

CLANG!

SMASH!

TWO HOURS LATER...

MAXWELL! WHAT ON EARTH IS GOING ON? WHAT HAVE YOU DONE TO MY PRIZE ANTIQUE STEINWAY PIANO?

ERM...

THAT PIANO ONCE BELONGED TO BOBBY CRUSH - AND WAS WORTH OVER TEN THOUSAND POUNDS!

BUT DAD - I HAVE TO GET INTO THE GUINNESS BOOK OF RECORDS!

WELL IN THAT CASE, I THINK I CAN HELP YOU THERE, SON.

HELLO? MR. McSQUIRTER? WOULD YOU POP ROUND PLEASE, MY SON'S ABOUT TO BREAK A RECORD - AND WE'D LIKE YOU TO VERIFY IT.

SHORTLY...

WHAT AM I GOING TO DO? MASAHARU TATSUSHIRO RAN 100m ON ONE FOOT STILTS IN 14.15 SECONDS! LET ME GET MY STILTS FROM THE SHED - I'LL HAVE A CRACK AT THAT ONE.

NO, SON.

WHEN I'VE FINISHED WITH YOU, YOU'LL BE IN THE GUINNESS BOOK OF RECORDS... WITH THE WORLD'S SOREST ARSE!!

HEY WOW!

'ODD JOB' BOB A-JOB BOB

HE DOES ODD JOBS FOR THE ODD BOB!

BOB, WILL YOU TAKE TOWSER, MY VALUABLE PRIZE WINNING PEDIGREE DOG FOR A WALK?

YES

BUT YOU MUST BRING HIM BACK BY THREE O'CLOCK AS HE HAS AN IMPORTANT VISITOR

YES, OF COURSE!

SNIFF! SNIFF!

SO... COME ON, TOWSER. LET'S GO TO THE PARK!

YIP! YIP!

WHOOSH! CRUNCH!

OH, BUNNIES! TOWSER HAS BEEN STRUCK BY A METEORITE FROM OUTER SPACE! HE'S AS DEAD AS A DODO!

NOW I'LL HAVE TO FIND AN IDENTICAL DOG, OR GRANNY WILLIS WILL HAVE MY GUTS FOR GARTERS!

SO...

D'S PETS

VALUABLE PEDIGREE DOGS £10

BAH!!

I CAN'T AFFORD THAT!

INSIDE...

EXCUSE ME. IF I DO SOME ODD JOBS IN YOUR SHOP, WILL YOU GIVE ME ONE OF THOSE DOGS IN YOUR WINDOW?

WELL, I DON'T SEE WHY NOT... NOW THEN... THE PARROTS HAVE ALL GOT CHRONIC DIARRHOEA AT THE MOMENT. YOU CAN CLEAN OUT THE BOTTOM OF THEIR AVIARY!

OH... ER...

DON'T FORGET YOUR BRUSH!

TWO HOURS LATER...

BAH!

THERE! I'M ALL FINISHED

LOVELY! YOU'VE DONE A GOOD JOB. HERE'S YOUR DOG

YIP YIP YIP!!

SO... COME ON, TOWSER. LET'S GO AND MEET YOUR NEW MISTRESS

YIP YIP YIP!!

BUT...

OH, LORDY! THEY LOOK A BIT FIERCE!

GR-RRRRRRR!!!

CRUMBS! THEY'RE COMING TOWARDS ME! I MUST PROTECT TOWSER AT ALL COSTS!

GR-RRRR!!

RIP GNASH TEAR

AND...

SHORTLY... HERE WE ARE, TOWSER! SAFE AND SOUND, AND ON THE STROKE OF THREE!

YIP YIP YIP!!

AH, BOB! RIGHT ON TIME. I HOPE MY LITTLE TOWSER HASN'T BEEN ANY TROUBLE

NOT AT ALL!

HERE'S TOWSER'S VISITOR NOW! CRUMBS, A VET! I HOPE NOTHING IS WRONG!

YIP YIP YIP!!

OH NO! HE'S PERFECTLY HEALTHY... ...I JUST DON'T LIKE HIM ANYMORE. I'D RATHER HAVE A BROWN ONE

BANG!

SNIFF! SNIFF! OH POOR TOWSER! SOB! I'LL MISS HIM SO MUCH! SOB! SNIFF!

WILL YOU DO ONE MORE THING FOR ME, SONNY?

SHORTLY... THANK YOU YOUNG MAN! THAT WAS A LOVELY SERVICE. HERE'S SOMETHING FOR YOUR TROUBLE!

TOWSER

CRIKEY! A BOB!

POSTMAN PLOD

 MMM.... WELL I NEVER. EEH... THAT'S INTERESTING... OOOH! HEH HEH HEH!

 BLOODY HELL! HA HA HA!! I DON'T BELIEVE IT!

 ARE! THAT'S A SHAME. WHAT A PITY... MMM... NEVER MIND

 OOOOH! WELL I NEVER! GOOD MORNING POSTIE. ANY MAIL FOR US?

 ERM... YEAH, JUST THIS ONE FOR YOUR HUSBAND... HANG ON A SECOND. I'M NEARLY FINISHED

 IT'S FROM THAT BIRD HE'S BEEN SHAGGING IN BRIGHTON. LOOKS LIKE HE'S GOT HER UP THE DUFF, THE DIRTY BASTARD

 GEOFFREY!! I WANT A WORD WITH YOU!! RIP

 MORE BILLS FOR ME, EH POSTIE? AFRAID SO MR BROWN. LET'S SEE... ELECTRICITY - SEVENTY QUID... BRITISH TELECOM - SIXTY TWO

 EXCUSE ME, BUT THOSE ARE ADDRESSED TO ME. YOU'VE GOT NO RIGHT TO... HEY! LOOK AT THIS... YOUR CREDIT CARD! OOPS! IT'S A RED ONE... 'FINAL DEMAND'... TWO GRAND!! FUCK ME! YOU'RE IN THE SHIT, MATE

 GIVE ME THOSE AT ONCE, DO YOU HEAR ME !? TWO GRAND EH? HMMMM....

 HEY! MR JONES! YOU COULD LEND MR BROWN HERE A COUPLE OF GRAND COULDN'T YOU? EH? RIP!! WHAT DO YOU MEAN?

 COME ON! YOU'RE FUCKING LOADED YOU ARE. LOOK AT THIS BANK STATEMENT... HOW DARE YOU!?! THAT'S STRICTLY CONFIDENTIAL!

HE'S GOT MONEY IN THE BUILDING SOCIETY AS WELL YOU KNOW. HE HAD A CHEQUE FROM THEM LAST WEEK THIS IS AN ABSOLUTE DISGRACE! I SHALL BE REPORTING THIS!

 LATER... IS THAT FOR ME? YES... AND IT'S FROM THE POOLS BY THE LOOK OF IT

 HANG ON... I'LL OPEN IT FOR YOU RIP! OH... ERM... THAT'S KIND OF YOU

 YOU LUCKY OLD BAG! EIGHT SCORE DRAWS! YOU'VE WON A MILLION QUID!! OOOH! I HAVEN'T, HAVE I?

 NAAAH! COURSE NOT, Y'DAFT COW. IT'S FROM THE HOSPITAL YOUR COLOSTOMY BAG'S ARRIVED. THEY CAN PLUMB IT IN FOR YOU NEXT TUESDAY

 SHORTLY... HMMM... PLAIN BROWN WRAPPER. THIS LOOKS INTERESTING

 HEH HEH HEH! BINGO!

 HEY! MR. SIMPSON. YOUR WANK MAGS HAVE ARRIVED! EUROPEAN XXXX SEX RED HOT THEY ARE TOO!

 LATER, BACK AT THE SORTING OFFICE... AH! PLOD. I WANT A WORD WITH YOU MAP OF COLCHESTER

 I'VE RECEIVED OVER 200 COMPLAINTS ABOUT YOUR BEHAVIOUR - IN THE LAST WEEK ALONE. YOU'VE BEEN OPENING MAIL, STEALING MONEY, USING ABUSIVE LANGUAGE, ASSAULTING CUSTOMERS, DAMAGING PROPERTY, URINATING IN GARDENS. THE LIST GOES ON AND ON COMPLAINTS

 LET'S FACE IT. YOU'RE LAZY, YOU'RE RUDE, YOU'RE INCOMPETENT. INDEED, YOU'RE TOTALLY UNEQUIPPED TO DEAL WITH THE GENERAL PUBLIC THERE'S NO PLACE FOR PEOPLE LIKE YOU IN TODAY'S DYNAMIC GO-AHEAD ROYAL MAIL DELIVERY SERVICE.

 SO... I'D LIKE TO BUY A STAMP PLEASE CHEQUES PAYABLE TO POST OFFICE COUNTERS (NO CHEQUES ACCEPTED) POSTAL CHARGES FOR TODAY SERVICES NOT AVAILABLE AT THIS OFFICE FUCK OFF. THIS POSITION'S CLOSED PLEASE QUEUE HERE, OUT THE DOOR, ROUND THE CORNER, PAST THE CINEMA, DOWN THE HIGH STREET AND ONTO THE RING ROAD

74

THE ADVENTURES OF THE HUMAN LEAGUE IN OUTER SPACE

PHIL   THE GIRLS

BALSA BOY

58 YEAR OLD SOCIAL INADEQUATE ARTHUR TRUBSHAW HAD ALWAYS DREAMT OF HAVING A CHILD OF HIS OWN. AND THE DAY HE BOUGHT A LARGE QUANTITY OF BALSA WOOD AND SOME STRING, THAT DREAM CAME TRUE...

THERE WE ARE. A SON OF MY OWN. I'LL CALL HIM...

BALSA BOY!

GEE! LOOK AT ME. I'M ALIVE. JUST LIKE A REAL BOY!

YES SON. THAT'S RIGHT. COME ON, I'LL TAKE YOU TO THE PARK AND YOU CAN PLAY WITH THE OTHER CHILDREN

AT THE PARK...

GEE DADDY! CAN I PLAY ON THE SWINGS?

HEY! WAIT FOR ME!

HOLD TIGHT BALSA BOY! LET'S SEE HOW HIGH YOU CAN GO

ARE YOU READY? WHOOSH!!

GEE DAD! WATCH ME FLYING HIGH IN THE SKY

SNAP!

CLONK!

OOF!

I PRESUME THIS PIECE OF WOOD WHICH JUST HIT MY DAUGHTER ON THE HEAD BELONGS TO THAT RIDICULOUS PUPPET OF YOURS

SAY SORRY TO THE LITTLE GIRL, BALSA BOY

GEE, I'M SORRY LITTLE GIRL. PERHAPS YOU'D LIKE TO COME TO MY HOUSE FOR TEA

MUMMY. I'M SCARED

COME ON DARLING. I'M TAKING YOU HOME

LATER...

GEE DADDY! LOOK AT ME

HERE I COME... WEEEE!!!

FLUMP!

HERE SON. I'LL HELP YOU UP

SHORTLY...

LOOK DAD. THOSE BOYS ARE PLAYING FOOTBALL

YES SON. GO ON, YOU CAN JOIN IN

BALSA BOY WILL PLAY IN GOAL, WON'T YOU, BALSA BOY

YES DAD

GO ON BALSA BOY! YOU CAN SAVE IT

BOOT!

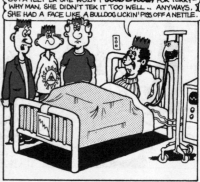

MORE 'UNINTELLIGENCE' JOKES AND SWEARING WITH

TERRY FUCKWITT

OOER! MY 'A' LEVEL RESULTS HAVE ARRIVED AT LAST. I HOPE I'VE DONE WELL

I NEED TWO 'A's AND A 'B' TO GET INTO LOUGHBOROUGH UNIVERSITY TO STUDY MATERIAL SCIENCE...

RIP!!

MMM...

TERRY!

THAT IS A GAS BILL. YOU ARE A FUCK WIT, AND THIS...

...IS A PUNCH IN THE FACE

BIFF!

YOU DIDN'T TAKE ANY 'A' LEVELS TERRY. YOU WERE THROWN OUT OF SCHOOL IN 1976

YOU HAVEN'T GOT ENOUGH SENSE TO GO TO THE TOILET, NEVER MIND UNIVERSITY

AT BEST YOU ARE A FUCKING IMBECILE. AT WORST, A CLUELESS CUNT. NOW PLEASE GO AWAY

EXCUSE ME YOUNG MAN, I THINK YOUR FATHER HAS BEEN SOMEWHAT HASTY IN HIS JUDGEMENT. I AM A CARING, CHRISTIAN YOUTH WORKER, A CHARITABLE AND COMPASSIONATE MAN OF EXTRAORDINARY VISION.

I THINK I RECOGNISE A GREAT UNTAPPED POTENTIAL IN YOU WHICH OTHERS HAVE FAILED TO SEE

MMM... ON SECOND THOUGHTS... NO

YOU ARE A COMPLETE AND UTTER DIM WIT

I MAY BE THICK, BUT I'M NOT A TOTAL SHIT FOR BRAINS! I'M SURE THERE'S SOMETHING USEFUL I CAN DO

MOTHER. I'M GOING TO HELP YOU WASH THE DISHES

A COUPLE OF THINGS WORTH MENTIONING, TERRY. FIRST OF ALL I DON'T HAVE ANY DISHES.

YOU MAY RECALL YOU WASHED THEM ALL LAST WEEK - WITH YOUR FATHER'S HAMMER

SECONDLY, I'M NOT YOUR MOTHER. SHE LIVES NEXT DOOR, AND SO DO YOU.

AND FINALLY...

I'M GOING TO HIT YOU VERY HARD ON THE HEAD WITH A CRICKET BAT

SMACK!

SO... I'LL DO THE WASHING, AND YOU CAN DO THE DRYING EH?

LATER...

FUCK ME, READERS. I HAVEN'T GOT THE BRAINS I WAS BORN WITH

GOOD NEWS TERRY!

EH?

I HAVE DEVISED A WAY IN WHICH EVEN A TOTAL PIG IGNORANT GIT LIKE YOURSELF CAN MAKE HIMSELF USEFUL!

ME AND MR JONES ARE GOING FOR A ROUND OF GOLF. YOU CAN BE OUR CADDY

GREAT!

HERE. YOU'LL NEED TO WEAR THESE ROLLER SKATES...

... ON YOUR HANDS

?

SHORTLY...

MMM... I THINK I'LL USE A LOFTED CLUB HERE...

...A NINE IRON PERHAPS

JONATHON RINGPIECE

I'M AS CONTROVERSIAL AS... ...FUCK!

THERE. I SAID IT!

I'M GOING TO BE PRETTY DAMN CONTROVERSIAL TODAY READERS!

I'M GOING TO USE A FOUR LETTER WORD!

SORRY TO DISAPPOINT YOU SONNY BUT THIS IS AN ADULT COMIC. IT'S PAGES ARE PEPPERED WITH WORDS LIKE FUCK

EH?

POLYTECHNIC LECTURER IN MEDIA STUDIES

EVEN THE OCCASIONAL USE OF THE WORD CUNT HAS FAILED TO PROVOKE ANY SIGNIFICANT PUBLIC OUTCRY

LATER... WELL, IF SWEARING WON'T CAUSE A RUMPUS I CAN ALWAYS TALK OPENLY AND EXPLICITLY ABOUT SEX

THAT'S BOUND TO RUFFLE A FEW FEATHERS!

FIRST, LET'S TALK ABOUT THAT OLD CHESTNUT PENIS SIZE. I THINK A LOT OF PEOPLE SUFFER HANG UPS ABOUT THE SIZE OF THEIR DICKS

NONE OF THE GIRLS I HAVE SEXUAL INTERCOURSE WITH EVER MENTION THE SIZE OF MY COCK.

NEXT I'M GOING TO TALK ABOUT WOMEN'S VAGINAS, ORAL SEX AND ABOUT MUTUAL MASTURBATION

HEY! AREN'T YOU GOING TO COMPLAIN? YOUR DAUGHTER'S A BIT YOUNG TO BE EXPOSED TO THIS KIND OF STUFF, DON'T YOU THINK?

NO, NOT AT ALL. MY DAUGHTER KNOWS ALL ABOUT SEX, BOTH HETROSEXUAL AND HOMOSEXUAL. SHE'S HEARD ALL ABOUT IT ON CHANNEL 4's 'SEX TALK'

WHY, SHE'S EVEN FAMILIAR WITH TERMS SUCH AS RIMMING, FILCHING AND GOLDEN SHOWERS, AREN'T YOU PETAL?

THAT'S RIGHT MUMMY

I HAVE NO INHIBITIONS ABOUT SEX WHATSOEVER

TSSCH! SOME DAYS YOU JUST CAN'T PROVOKE A STORM OF PROTEST!

LATER... HEY! I'VE CRACKED IT READERS! I'M GOING TO BE A CONTROVERSIAL POP STAR JUST LIKE MADONNA!

I'VE WRITTEN A SONG ABOUT CHRISTIANITY AND IT'S BOUND TO OFFEND THE MORAL MAJORITY!

WAIT TILL YOU HEAR THIS...

OOH! I WANNA GO TO BED WITH JESUS. OOOH! I WANNA KISS AND FEEL HIS BOTTOM. OOH YEAH!

WELL, WHAT DID YOU THINK OF THAT THEN? PRETTY BLOODY CONTROVERSIAL I'D SAY, EH?

I'M AFRAID YOU PICKED THE WRONG MAN TO PLAY IT TO.

I'M THE BISHOP OF DURHAM, AND QUITE FRANKLY I DON'T GIVE A MONKEY'S TOSS ABOUT YOUR SONG

IN FACT I QUITE LIKE IT. IT ENCOURAGES DEBATE ABOUT THE CHURCH, AND THAT HAS GOT TO BE HEALTHY. I BELIEVE IT IS A POLEMICAL HYMN, IF YOU WILL.

SHORTLY... THIS CAN'T FAIL! I'M GOING TO BE A MODERN ARTIST. AND I'M PAINTING A CONTROVERSIAL PORTRAIT OF THE QUEEN!

HMM... IT'S NOT QUITE RIGHT. THERE'S SOMETHING MISSING...

I KNOW WHAT IT NEEDS!

A GREAT BIG TURD SLAP BANG IN THE MIDDLE OF THE CANVAS!

HNNNGH!!

JUST WAIT TILL THE CRITICS SEE THIS. THEY'LL BE UP IN ARMS!

AT THE ART GALLERY...

IT'S THE QUEEN. I CRAPPED ON IT. PRETTY CONTROVERSIAL EH?

WELL... IT WOULD HAVE BEEN A FEW WEEKS AGO...

BUT THIS MONTH 'FAECES PORTRAITURE' IS ALL THE RAGE. IN FACT THE QUEEN HAS BOUGHT SEVERAL WORKS RENDERED IN EXCREMENT ON CANVAS FOR HER OWN PRIVATE COLLECTION

I'M AFRAID IT'S OLD HAT

I KNOW! I'LL POSE NAKED WITH MY SON, JUST LIKE SINEAD O'CONNOR. NOW SHE IS CONTROVERSIAL!

I SUPPORT THE I.R.A.

BLOODY HELL! THIS IS RIDICULOUS

THAT'S ENOUGH OF YOUR SWEARING YOUNG MAN

SMACK!

HOW DARE YOU USE VIOLENCE AGAINST THAT CHILD!

WAH!

DIDN'T YOU KNOW THIS IS NATIONAL NO SPANKING WEEK

NEXT DAY...

HEH HEH HEH!

MAN SMACKS SON'S BOTTOM SHOCK!

CONTROVERSY RAGES OVER CORPORAL PUNISHMENT FOR KIDS

PRETTY CONTROVERSIAL, EH?

DALEY Starr

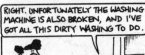

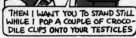

88

TUBBY JOHNSON

OKAY, BOYS. THAT'S IT FOR THIS PERIOD. OFF YOU GO TO YOUR NEXT LESSON. P.E.

SIR...SIR...I'VE EATEN SO MUCH CHOCOLATE AND LARD THAT I'VE BECOME JAMMED IN MY SEAT....

...I'LL HAVE TO MISS GAMES, SIR! (SNIGGER)

THAT WON'T BE NECESSARY, JOHNSON! YOU'VE FORGOTTEN THAT THIS IS A WOODWORK CLASS...

HUNH!?!

...I'LL BE ABLE TO CUT YOU FREE!

BAH!!!

SO... JOHNSON! WHERE'S YOUR KIT, BOY?

PLEASE, SIR! I'VE FORGOTTEN IT! I'LL HAVE TO MISS GAMES

NO NEED FOR THAT, BOY! YOU CAN USE THESE COMEDY ELEPHANT SHORTS I BORROWED FROM THE CIRCUS!

BUT SIR, I'VE GOT A NOTE, TOO

LET'S SEE...PLEASE EXCUSE TUBBY FROM GAMES AS HE IS FAT. SIGNED, TUBBY'S MUM

HMMMM!!

THIS NOTE DOESN'T FOOL ME, BOY. FOR A START, IT'S WRITTEN ON THE BACK OF AN INDUS-TRIAL DOUGHNUT WRAPPER!!

OH, BUNNIES!

NOW GET ON THAT FIELD!!

BAH!

ON THE FIELD... RIGHT, THEN, TIMPSON, SYKES! YOU PICK TEAMS

OKAY. I'LL HAVE SMITHY...

TWO MINUTES LATER

COUGH! WHEEZE

ER...

...WE'LL HAVE ME PASTRY

BAH! THAT MEANS WE'VE GOT JOHNSON! IT'S NOT FAIR!

SHORTLY...

RIGHT, BOYS! LET'S HAVE AN EGG AND SPOON RACE

PLEASE, SIR! WE CAN'T...

GPD. ST. SD 12.90   VIZ 47

...JOHNSON HAS EATEN ALL THE EGGS, SIR!

BARP!!

...AND THE SPOONS

HMM! RIGHT! EVERYONE FIND A PARTNER. WE'RE GOING TO DO LEAPFROG PRACTICE!

I'LL PARTNER YOU, WIDDLE!

ERM...

...OH, DEAR!

SO... THAT'S RIGHT, JOHNSON. BUILD UP A GOOD SPEED. BRACE YOURSELF, WIDDLE

PUFF, PANT

CRUMBS!

NER NER NER NER

PRESENTLY...

OKAY, BOYS. LET'S HAVE A THREE LEGGED RACE. THERE'S A BIG CAKE FOR THE WINNERS

COR!!

ON YOUR MARKS... ...GET SET...

BANG!

WHAA...

GOSH!!

THAT'S A NEW SCHOOL RECORD, TUBBY! YOU'VE WON THE CAKE

WHAP! WHAP! WHAP!

BUT... OH, I FORGOT TO TELL YOU, TUBBY. IT'S A CAKE OF SOAP. HO HO HO

BAH! COUGH! CHOKE!

91

QUICK! PRETEND YOU'RE OUT! IT'S...

PRAISE THE LORD!

IVAN JELICAL

WHAT A SPLENDID MORNING GOD HAS GIVEN US. I SHALL NOW SPREAD HIS WORD AMONGST THE SINNERS OF PONDICHERRY CRESCENT.

BUGGER! IT'S A GOD-BOTHERER!

KNOCK! KNOCK!

GOD BLESS YOU SON, AND PRAISE BE TO THE LORD.

PRAAIIISE HIIIM! BLESSED ARE THE CHILDREN.

ME MAM SAYS SHE'S NOT IN.

SLAM!

DING! DONG!

12

OH WHAT JOY BEING A FISHER OF MEN!

DING! DONG!

HAVE YOU EVER THOUGHT THAT AT ANY TIME YOU MAY BE CALLED BEFORE YOUR CREATOR TO ATONE FOR YOUR SINS, AND YEA IT IS WRITTEN THAT YOU MAY BE CONDEMNED TO EVERLASTING TORMENT IN THE LAKE OF FIRE.

BIFF!

GUHN!

BROTHER, YOU HAVE DELIVERED AN MIGHTY BLOW UNTO THINE NEIGHBOUR'S EYE. YET SHALL I SEEK NO VENGENCE; EXODUS 2 verse 13:14...

VERILY AS A CHRISTIAN I MUST TURN THE OTHER CHEEK; DEREK 3,13.

FORGIVE HIM FATHER, FOR HE KNOWS NOT WHAT HE HAS DONE.

NOK! NOK!

14

STORE YE UP NOT EARTHLY TREASURES, CONSIDER THE LILLIES OF THE FIELD, THEY DO NOT TOIL, YET SOLOMON IN ALL HIS GLORY WAS NEVER MORE RADIANT...

ARE YOU TAKING THE PISS? I'M ON NIGHTS.

EMPHYSEMA 12 verse 18-19...

BAM!

NEXT DOOR...

16

BRRIING!

HAVE YOU SURRENDERED YOUR HEART TO JESUS? DO YOU KNOW THAT GOD LOVES YOU AND THAT HIS LOVE IS THE WORD AND HIS WORD IS ALL AROUND YOU, AND YOU ONLY HAVE TO ASK AND HE WILL COME UNTO YOU AND HIS LOVE SHALL BE LIKE UNTO AN DOVE THAT DESCENDETHED DOWN UNTO THE EARTH...

AND THAT AFTER FORTY DAYS AND FORTY NIGHTS HIS LOVE SHALLETH BE-ETH ...ERM... FORTY CUBITS LONG AND SHALL BE THRICE TEMPTED SAYING COMING UNTO HIM THAT WHOETH SHALL BE WITHOUT SIN LET HIM REMOVE THE MOTE FROM THINE EYE WITHOUT FIRST REMOVING THE CAMEL FROM THE EYE OF THE GATES OF HEAVEN? PENECILLIAN 13 verse 27-31

YES, I DID KNOW THAT. I COULDN'T AGREE WITH YOU MORE YOUNG MAN, YOU SEE, I'M THE VICAR OF THIS PARISH.

THE VICARAGE

GOOD DAY.

16

CLUNK!

THE LORD HIS FILLED MY HEART WITH MUSIC AND BADE ME SPREAD HIS GOSPELL UNTIL MY CUP FLOWETH OVER AND RUNNETH UPON STONY GROUND.

RAP! RAP!

18

I'M GOING TO LAY DOWN MY TROUBLES, DOWN BY THE RIVERSIDE! DOWN BY THE RIVERSIDE! DOWN BY THE RIVERSIDE!

I'M GOING TO LAY DOWN MY TROUBLES, DOWN BY THE RIVERSIDE, AND I AIN'T GOING TO STUDY WAR NO MORE!

10 MINUTES LATER... I'M GOING TO LAY RIGHT DOWN WITH JESUS, DOWN BY THE RIVERSIDE!

DOWN BY THE RI - VER - SIIIDE!!!

NATIONAL DEAF AND DUMB INSTITUTE

?

AT HOME... IT'S GOOD TO BE ALIVE. GOD IS LOVE, AND HE FILLS MY HEART WITH JOY. IF ONLY EVERYONE COULD KNOW THE JOY AND GLORY WHICH HIS WORD BRINGS UNTO ME.

INDEED I AM A WEALTHY MAN.

2 HOURS LATER...

LATER STILL...

ROGER IRRELEVANT

HE'S STILL COMPLETELY HATSTAND.

THAT'S ODD — WHERE HAS THE TIN-OPENER GONE?

I EXPECT ROGER'S GOT IT, DAD. HE INVITED A NUMBER OF KITCHEN UTENSILS UP TO HIS ROOM TO JOIN HIM FOR A COFFEE MORNING.

MY ADVICE IS FOR YOU TO POP UPSTAIRS AND KICK HIS TEETH IN.

..SO I SAID TO HER, I SAID "CONIFER TREE?", I SAID, "YOU'RE NO MORE A CONIFER TREE THAN I AM", AND SHE SAID...

LOOK, SON, GET OUT OF THE HOUSE FOR A WHILE, EH? GO FOR A WALK OR SOMETHING.

I'M VERY TIRED, AND YOUR RATHER SLENDER GRIP ON REALITY IS MAKING ME FEEL A LITTLE DISORIENTATED.

SO, SHORTLY –

NOW FOR SOME MERRY LARKS WITH MY TIME-TRAVELLING SPHINCTER, EH CHUMS?

?

OH LOOK! IT'S A HIGH-RANKING V.I.P. ON AN INFORMAL 'WALKABOUT'

WHY, SO IT IS!

VLART VLART

HELLO THERE, YOUNG MAN, AND WHAT DO YOU DO, EXACTLY?

I SEE. THAT'S VERY INTERES...

OHO! SO, MY EVIL STEPMOTHER RETURNS TO CHEAT ME OUT OF MY INHERITANCE!

WELL IT WON'T WORK! THESE FROGS ARE MINE, YOU HEAR ME? THEY'RE ALL MINE!

THE GENTLE INSERTION OF THIS PIECE OF SHORTBREAD INTO YOUR NOSE WILL DEAL WITH YOU...

...YOU FICKLE WHORE!!

CONSTABLE, I AM A HIGH-RANKING V.I.P. AND THAT YOUTH HAS JUST PHYSICALLY ASSAULTED ME. PLEASE ARREST HIM IMMEDIATELY.

DON'T WORRY SIR. I'LL HANDLE THIS.

RIGHT, SUNSHINE, ARE YOU GOING TO HAND OVER THOSE BISON, OR DO I HAVE TO HIT YOU AGAIN?!

TCHAH! THAT PEST MIRIAM STOPPARD HAS BEEN CHEWING MY BEST ARMCHAIR AGAIN!

HELLO? DOCTOR. I'M 'IN CONTINENT'

95

Get into her knickers with Interflower.

With bouquets starting at only £10,
there's no better way to get your fingers and tops.

THE PHANTOM OF FAIRPOOLS

BURLY LUMBERJACK BILL CARTER AND HIS YOUNG SON JIM WERE ON A CAMPING HOLIDAY NEAR THE LAKESIDE TOWN OF FAIRPOOLS...

THAT'S THE TENT SET UP — COME ON JIM, I'LL TAKE YOU FISHING.

RIGHTO, DAD

DAD! THAT OLD MAN — HE LOOKS ILL!

ACCCCHH... AHHH... FRIGGINNORA...

JIM RUSHED OVER TO HELP THE MYSTERIOUS STRANGER

EY, COULD YE LEND US A COUPLE O'SHILLINGS FORRA CUPPA TEA GOD BLESS YE LAD?

IT'S FOR ME BUS FARE, SEE... THEY..I..I LEFT ME WALLET IN THE CHURCH, LIKE

KIND-HEARTED JIM GAVE HIS HOLIDAY SPENDING MONEY TO THE PECULIAR OLD GENTLEMAN

AAH CHEERS SON THASS GRAND HAVE A SWIG O' THIS GOD BLESS YE

EY MATES.. ..MATES.. SEE THIS..

LOOK WHAT THE OLD MAN GAVE ME, DAD! WHATEVER CAN IT BE?

WELL JIM, IT SEEMS TO BE SOME KIND OF EMPTY ALUMINIUM CANNISTER

ALTHOUGH I'VE NEVER SEEN ANYTHING QUITE LIKE IT BEFORE

GOSH! DO YOU SUPPOSE IT'S VERY OLD?

COULD BE, JIM COME ON — LET'S GET DOWN TO THE LAKE

THIS IS GOOD FUN!

YES

SUDDENLY, BILL STARTED HACKING AT THE BOTTOM OF THE BOAT WITH A CLAW HAMMER

HA HA HA! GO FOR IT, DAD!

OH NO! WATER'S POURING INTO THE BOAT — WE'LL SURELY BE DROWNED!

WAIT! THE OLD MAN'S CANNISTER... I-I THINK I'VE GOT AN IDEA!

QUICK AS A FLASH, THE PLUCKY YOUNG LAD JAMMED THE METALLIC CYLINDER INTO THE JAGGED HOLE IN THE BOTTOM OF THE BOAT

BIZARRE! IT'S PREVENTING MOST OF THE WATER FROM COMING INTO THE BOAT!

MORE OR LESS

MM, YES LIKE A SORT OF MAKESHIFT STOPPER, OR BUNG.

USING ALL HIS STRENGTH, BRAWNY BILL CARTER ROWED BACK TO THE SHORE

WE MUST FIND THAT REMARKABLE OLD MAN AND THANK HIM

IF HE HADN'T GIVEN ME THE CANNISTER WE WOULD HAVE DROWNED!

THAT'S ODD — HE WAS RIGHT HERE LESS THAN AN HOUR AGO. WE'D BETTER ASK SOMEONE WHERE HE IS

IT'S ALMOST...EERIE... THE WAY HE ISN'T HERE ANYMORE..

NO, I'M AFRAID I DON'T KNOW OF ANY OLD MAN LIVING ROUND THESE PARTS

BUT THEN, YOU SEE, I'M A STRANGER HERE MYSELF. I'M ONLY IN FAIRPOOLS ON A DAY TRIP

BUT HE WAS REAL, I TELL YOU! AS REAL AS YOU OR I!

I SAW THAT OLD MAN MYSELF — WITH MY VERY OWN EYES!

MR CARTER, I AM A SCIENTIST. IT IS MY JOB TO EXPLAIN THE WORLD AROUND US — THE WORLD WE SEE, HEAR AND TOUCH.

BUT I CAN GIVE NO SCIENTIFIC EXPLANATION AS TO WHO — OR WHAT — IT WAS YOU SAW TODAY.

HE'S RIGHT JIM, WE WILL PROBABLY NEVER REALLY UNDERSTAND.

ALL WE CAN DO IS BE GRATEFUL — GRATEFUL FOR THIS CHANCE TO REBUILD OUR LIVES!

Billy the Fish

BILLY "THE FISH" THOMSON- FULCHESTER UNITED'S BRILLIANT AQUATIC KEEPER- HAS BEEN ROCKETED TO STARDOM AFTER VIEWERS SAW HIM CRYING ON TV.

BUT WHEN HIS AGENT AND PROMOTER FRANK McSPORRAN IS SHOT DEAD, THE FINGER OF SUSPICION POINTS AT BILLY....

COME WITH ME THOMSON, YOU'RE GOING AWAY FOR A VERY LONG TIME.

BUT... BUT... I NEVER DID IT! I WAS AT MY COUSIN'S HOUSE.

?

OH! BLEEP! I DON'T BELIEVE IT!

IT'S TV PRANKSTER JEREMY BEADLE! AGAIN.

HEY!

WE'RE ALL SICK OF YOU AND YOUR PATHETIC PRANKS, BEADLE. NOW IT'S YOUR TURN TO WATCH OUT... TOMMY'S ABOUT!

SMACK!

TAKE THAT!

THANKS TOMMY. THESE LAST FEW DAYS HAVE BEEN A HARROWING EXPERIENCE FOR ME.

WELL, THAT'S THE LAST WE'LL SEE OF HIM, BILLY.

YOU NEED A REST BILLY. I WANT YOU TO TAKE A FEW DAYS OFF.

TELL YOU WHAT, WHY NOT POP UP TO MY SUMMER RETREAT? I OWN A SMALL LOG CABIN IN FULCHESTER'S HEAVILY WOODED SUBURB OF PIN TWEAKS.

GREAT! I CAN GO FISHING. I LOVE FISHING, ME.

THE NEXT DAY...

YOU ARE ENTERING PIN TWEAKS

AH, THIS IS THE LIFE! A NICE RELAXING DAY'S FISHING FAR AWAY FROM THE HUSTLE, BUSTLE, AND PRESSURES OF THE WORLD OF LEAGUE FOOTBALL.

HELLO. WHAT'S THAT ON THE SHORE OVER THERE?

WHY- IT'S A GIRL'S BODY WRAPPED IN POLYTHENE!

I'D BETTER CALL THE SHERRIF.

HOURS LATER, IN THE MORTUARY...

DO YOU KNOW WHO SHE IS SHERRIF?

YES BILLY. THIS IS LAURA PRESTON- COACH SYD PRESTON'S DAUGHTER.

GOSH! FULCHESTER'S CHEERLEADER AND MAY QUEEN LAURA PRESTON MURDERED! SYD WILL BE AS SICK AS A PARROT.

YES.

THERE'S SOMEONE I'D LIKE YOU TO MEET BILLY.

THIS IS FBI SPECIAL AGENT TOMMY COOPER. HE'S INVESTIGATING LAURA'S MURDER.

GLASS... BOTTLE. BOTTLE... GLASS.

MEANWHILE, IN FULCHESTER BOSS TOMMY BROWN'S OFFICE...

THANK-YOU SHERRIF. THANKS FOR LETTING ME KNOW.

BAD NEWS SYD. YOUR TEENAGE DAUGHTER LAURA HAS BEEN FOUND MURDERED AND WRAPPED IN POLYTHENE. SHE WAS ASSAULTED BY SEVERAL MEN BEFORE SHE DIED ALSO.

CRUMBS BOSS. THIS IS A REAL SICKENER. DO YOU THINK THEY'LL CATCH THE MURDERER?

I DON'T KNOW SYD. RIGHT NOW WE HAVE TO CONCENTRATE ALL OUR THOUGHTS ON SATURDAY'S VITAL F.A. CUP CLASH WITH TOTTERHAM HOTSHOTS.

THE COCKNEY HIGH-FLIERS WILL BE A TOUGH NUT TO CRACK, WITH ENGLAND STARS GARY SPINNAKER AND PAUL "GAZZA" GASKET IN THEIR LINE-UP.

FIXTURE LIST

YES. I'D BETTER CALL THE LADS IN FOR AN EXTRA TRAINING SESSION EH BOSS?

THAT AFTERNOON... SORRY TO HEAR ABOUT UM HEAP BAD MURDER OF YOUR DAUGHTER SYD.

THANKS BROWN FOX.

YES. SHE WAS RAPED BY THREE MEN WASN'T SHE?

APPARENTLY SO. IT'S CERTAINLY KNOCKED THE STUFFING OUT OF ME, I CAN TELL YOU!

ACTUALLY- I'D IMAGINE MY WIFE'S PRETTY UPSET TOO, I'VE BEEN MEANING TO GIVE HER A CALL ACTUALLY. I'LL DO IT AS SOON AS WE FINISH TRAINING.

BROWN FOX NOT KNOW LAURA THAT WELL.

OH, I DID.

IN FECT, I HAFF SEWERAL TAPE RECORDINKS OFF CONWERSATIONS I HED MITT HER, CONTAININK ZE ACCOUNTS OF HER DREAMS UND HER SEXUAL FENTASIES.

RIGHT LADS. LISTEN CAREFULLY. I'M GOING TO MAKE A FEW TACTICAL CHANGES FOR SATURDAY'S GAME.

WE'RE GOING TO USE THE CONTINENTAL SWEEPER SYSTEM. WE'LL HAVE A SPARE MAN AT THE BACK, PLAY THE LONG BALL UP THE MIDDLE AND USE THE FULL WIDTH OF THE PITCH.

WE'LL HAVE A FLOATING FLANKER AND A SPARE MAN BEHIND THE FRONT TWO TO PICK UP THE LOOSE BALL IN THE MIDDLE OF THE PARK.

STARS BEHIN

It used to be big news when a famous celebrity went to jail, but nowadays it seems to happen every day.

Lester Piggott, footballer Tony Adams. The list seems endless. For in today's materialistic world the temptation to commit crime is enormous, and nowhere more so than in show-business. Indeed for celebrities today prison sentences are looked on almost as an occupational hazard. One day they're appearing on TV and signing autographs, the next day they're sewing mailbags and slopping out.

PORRIDGE

So who are the stars most likely to fall foul of the law, and what kind of crimes might they commit? And how would today's top show-business stars cope with doing 'porridge'?

Just for fun, we asked Britain's top Show-business Criminology Psychoanalyst to answer these questions by examining the character of several top celebrities. And here, using his in-depth knowledge of crime and the stars, he gives us his verdicts.

Roly-poly TV astronomer **RUSSELL GRANT** looks innocent enough on the box. But I believe that if times were hard burly Russell could put himself about a bit, and turn to violent crime for his livelihood.

BREAD

I feel that Russell would go in at the deep end, and carry out an armed wages snatch on a Securicor van. But the flam-boyant star gazer would refuse to lie low after the raid, and would give himself away to police by throwing money around in London's West End clubs.

RICE

Russell would receive between 10 and 14 years for armed robbery, but I believe he would adjust easily to life inside. His amiable nature and generous personality would make him popular with other inmates. I think he would get a job in the prison library, and in his spare time do horoscopes for warders and perhaps even the governor. With good behaviour he would be out and back on our breakfast TV screens in about 7 years.

LLOYD-WEBBER

Taking and driving away a vehicle without the owner's consent may not sound like the most serious crime, but someone who commits that offence should be made an example of, especially if that person is TV magician **PAUL DANIELS**.

I believe that Paul, after a drinking session with other showbiz pals, could try to show off by stealing a high powered car and taking it for a joyride.

MAGICIAN

If Daniels was sent to prison for his crime he would find it a far cry from his glittering career as Britain's top magician. He would spend long periods of time banged up in a cell, and practising magic would not be easy. Prisoners are not allowed playing cards, rabbits, swords or strings of handkerchiefs in jail. I believe Daniels would become disillusioned, and after his release I believe he would soon be in constant trouble with police for various petty crimes.

BLACKBURN

If Italian gangsters were looking to launder mafia millions in Britain they may well turn to **TONY BLACKBURN**. And I believe that Tony is too nice a person to turn them away. He could unwittingly become tangled in a web of international fraud.

ROCHDALE

If the police rumbled Tony's illegal money laundering operation, then the popular former Radio One DJ would be in big trouble. Not only would he face a severe prison sentence, but his Sicilian paymasters may well try to silence him.

OLDHAM

Life inside would be a nightmare for pretty boy Blackburn, 47. As well as keeping his eyes open for mafia hit men, Tony would also have to watch out for all the red blooded criminals who have not set eyes on a women for many years. Loneliness drives men to do awful things behind prison walls, and for Tony the showers would be a no-go area. Indeed, Tony would have to be careful. Less attractive men than him have left jail with ringpieces like doughnuts.

BISCUITS

Shoplifting is the single most common crime among the stars of stage and screen. And if millionaire chat show

host **TERRY WOGAN** were wrongly accused of stealing a packet of biscuits and a pair of women's tights after a mix-up in Sainsbury's, few people in showbusiness would even turn an eye.

Should Terry receive a custodial sentence, he would find that as in the outside world, opportunities exist in side prison for the commercially minded. Terry has a sharp eye for business, and I believe that within days he would be dealing in tobacco, chocolate and pornographic magazines. The thrifty Irishman could then enjoy privileges such as a carpet and TV in his cell, and would have the warders as well as the inmates at his beck and call.

KNIFE

Children's TV artist **TONY HART** would be the last person you'd expect to find cruising the Kings Cross area in a pink cadillac, wearing a floppy hat. It's hard to believe, but if found guilty of living off immoral earnings, Vision On presenter Hart could receive a jail sentence of up to 5 years.

BARS

Sensitive Hart would never truly adjust to prison life. In fact, he would lie awake at nights planning his escape. One day, whilst working in the prison kitchen, I believe Hart would grab a knife and take a warder hostage. Eventually he would clamber onto the prison roof and stay there for several days, shouting abuse at police, throwing slates, and making imaginative use of old sheets and other materials to create brightly coloured, attractive banners proclaiming his innocence.

FORK

ESTHER RANTZEN has a reputation as a tireless campaigner for good causes, but I believe there are flaws to her character. If, for example, she were offered £5,000 by a crooked second-hand car dealer to murder a rival small time gangster, I believe she would carry out the killing, against the advice of her husband, BBC producer Desmond Wilcox.

Of course life would be the only sentence Esther could expect for the cold blooded contract slaying. I think she would be appalled by the conditions she found inside jail, and would immediately start campaigning for better conditions and facilities. I think Esther would genuinely regret her crime, and would become a model prisoner, studying for an Open University Psychology degree, and writing books. After only 7 years I think she would be out on parole.

SPOON

However, I fear Esther would very quickly be back inside, and this time for good. I believe she would have a huge row with her husband Desmond Wilcox after discovering that he had spent the £5,000, and after a struggle her gun would go off, fatally wounding her balding TV executive husband.

CELEBRITY COURT

THIS WEEK'S GUEST JUDGE

SIMON BATES

We were rather short of ideas for this issue, so just for fun we asked Britain's favourite DJ Simon Bates to be judge for a day and preside over some ficticious court cases, passing sentence on some well know celebrities who an imaginery jury have found guilty of committing hypothetical crimes.

Simes agreed to don his judge's wig and dish out justice in the following cases which we have made up.

⚖⚖⚖ ⚖⚖⚖

Defendant: **THE KRANKIES**
Charge: Sending obscene material through the post.

Verdict: **GUILTY**

Simes Sums Up: I'm as liberal as the next man, but due to the extremely sordid nature of the material concerned here I have no hesitation in sentencing Jimmy and Jeanette to the maximum term the law allows.

Simes Sentence: They will go to prison for 2 years.

⚖⚖⚖ ⚖⚖⚖

Defendant: **BERYL REID**
Charge: (Just for fun) Possession of a class A controlled substance with intent to supply.

Verdict: **GUILTY**

Simes Sums Up: Knowing Beryl as I do, I am particularly disappointed to find her before me on such a serious charge. However, this is only a first offence, and I feel confident that you have learnt your lesson. I propose to give you a second chance.

Simes Sentence: I hereby sentence you to 18 months in prison, suspended for 2 years. In addition the court will seize the estimated proceeds of your crimes – £7,500.

⚖⚖⚖ ⚖⚖⚖

Defendant: **BOB HOLNESS**
Charge: Drunk and Disorderly, Urinating in a public place.

Verdict: **GUILTY**

Simes Sums Up: I had always thought you were an intelligent man. But your behaviour here has reflected no intelligence on your part. A man in your position, a respected game show presenter, should set an example to others. You have let yourself and many other people down.

Simes Sentence: I hereby fine you £10,000, and also sentence you to 5 years in prison.

If any of the celebrities named feel that their sentences are unfair they can join in the courtroom drama by making a postal appeal. Simply write to: The Appeal Jury, Viz Celebrity Court of Justice (No. 46), P.O. Box 1PT, Newcastle upon Tyne NE99 1PT. Your appeals will be heard in the next issue, celebrity Judge and coffee ad star Gareth Hunt presiding.

The Undersea World of PAT ROACH out of Auf Wiedersehen, Pet

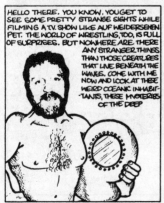

HELLO THERE. YOU KNOW, YOU GET TO SEE SOME PRETTY STRANGE SIGHTS WHILE FILMING A T.V. SHOW LIKE AUF WEIDERSEHEN PET. THE WORLD OF WRESTLING,TOO, IS FULL OF SURPRISES. BUT NOWHERE ARE THERE ANY STRANGER THINGS THAN THOSE CREATURES THAT LIVE BENEATH THE WAVES. COME WITH ME NOW AND LOOK AT THESE WEIRD OCEANIC INHABITANTS, THESE MYSTERIES OF THE DEEP

THIS IS A CERATOID ANGLER FISH. SHE USES A SPINE AS A LURE TO TEMPT FISH TOWARDS HER MOUTH. THE MALE IS TINY AND LIVES AS A PARASITE...

...HE STAYS ATTACHED TO HER BELLY FOR HIS WHOLE LIFE!

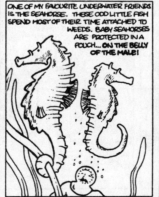

ONE OF MY FAVOURITE UNDERWATER FRIENDS IS THE SEAHORSE. THESE ODD LITTLE FISH SPEND MOST OF THEIR TIME ATTACHED TO WEEDS. BABY SEAHORSES ARE PROTECTED IN A POUCH... ON THE BELLY OF THE MALE!

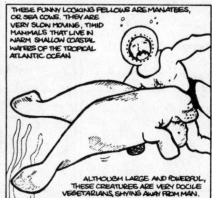

THESE FUNNY LOOKING FELLOWS ARE MANATEES, OR SEA COWS. THEY ARE VERY SLOW MOVING, TIMID MAMMALS THAT LIVE IN WARM SHALLOW COASTAL WATERS OF THE TROPICAL ATLANTIC OCEAN

ALTHOUGH LARGE AND POWERFUL, THESE CREATURES ARE VERY DOCILE VEGETARIANS, SHYING AWAY FROM MAN.

NEXT WEEK – TIMOTHY SPALL'S LIVING DESERT

102

LEAVE ME ALONE

A West Yorkshire man is claiming that presenters of a top BBC current affairs programme are making his life a misery.

For the last 12 years Stuart Lewerthwaite believes he has been the victim of a campaign of hate carried out by presenters of BBC2's flagship current affairs programme 'Newsnight'. His house has been burgled repeatedly, his property vandalised and threats made against his family.

CATALOGUE

Among a catalogue of allegations made to West Yorkshire police, Mr Lewerthwaite claims that:

● Suave Newsnight anchor man Jeremy Paxman has broken into his house on 3 occasions in the last 12 months, stealing property worth over £300, and damaging door and window locks.

● Glamorous newsreader Francine Stock kicked down garage doors at the rear of his property and stole garden tools, a bicycle and an aluminium stepladder which she later sold to sports presenter Desmond Lynam.

● Top news analyst Peter Snow drove a motorcycle across his front lawn at 2am on a Sunday morning, causing damage to flowerbeds.

● Various Newsnight reporters regularly congregate outside his house, smoking cigarettes and swinging on his gate. On one occasion an unidentified newsreader urinated against his garden wall.

DIRECTORY

According to Mr Lewerthwaite the trouble began as long ago as 1985 when a brick was thrown through his kitchen window. "I thought it was just kids but after a brief chase I cornered one of the culprits on waste ground near my house. I immediately recognised him as Peter Sissons, the then Newsnight presenter."

ENCYCLOPAEDIA

After a brief struggle Mr Lewerthwaite claims that Sissons escaped, bounding

ANOTHER SHOWBIZ EXCLUSIVE

over a fence and making a getaway on the back of a motorcycle driven by BBC political editor John Cole.

"I went straight to the police, but they told me it was just an isolated incident and there wasn't much they could do. I thought nothing more of it until 2 weeks later when somebody knocked at my front door." Mr Lewerthwaite was surprised to find highly rated Newsnight host Jeremy Paxman standing on the doorstep.

TOASTER

"He looked very nervous, and asked me if I had the time. He kept me talking for several minutes until I became suspicious and shut the door. I ran to the back of the house to find that the kitchen door had been forced open by Sue Lawley, and a toaster, a casserole dish and two pounds in cash had been stolen."

RAPPER

The next morning Mr Lewerthwaite phoned the BBC and spoke to the duty officer who logged his complaint. "To this day I've still heard nothing from them", he told us. "It's obvious that nothing is being done".

RANSACKED

A few months later Mr Lewerthwaite and his wife returned home from the pub to find their front door wide open. "The house had been ransacked. Our TV, video, music centre – everything was gone." Even items of clothing together with jewelry belonging to Mrs Lewerthwaite had been stolen.

OBSCENITIES

"All those things could be replaced", Mr Lewerthwaite told us. "But what really upset us was the obscenities which had been daubed on

Man begs Newsnight Bully Boys

Paxman – suave

Mr Lewerthwaite's house yesterday

Lawley – toaster

the walls by Peter Snow. And to make matters worse, when I tuned in to Newsnight that evening I saw Donald McCormack cockily wearing one of my white shirts, a present from my wife, stolen only hours earlier."

BONNET

The very next night the Lewerthwaites were awoken after midnight by banging sounds from outside. When Mr Lewerthwaite went to investigate he saw former 'Tonight' presenter Dennis Tuohey jumping up and down on the bonnet of his car. After chasing the veteran anchor man off, Mr Lewerthwaite discovered that the car had been broken into and a radio cassette, plus a dozen tapes, had been stolen.

BOOT

To date Mr Lewerthwaite has reported 71 incidents to police, all involving Newsnight presenters and associated TV journalists and correspondents. However West Yorkshire police have failed to make a single arrest.

FISHWIFE

A spokesman for the BBC's current affairs departmen refused to comment. Meanwhile Mr Lewerthwaite, who is 83 and lost the use of one eye during military service in 1942, vowed never to watch the Newsnight programme again. "In future I shall be watching the News at Ten", he told us

BEFORE WE FINALISE YOUR WILL, FARMER GILES, DO YOU BEQUEATH ANY MONEY TO YOUR BROTHER?

NO. HE GETS MY GOAT.

SOLICITOR

CD-ST-9.90.

CLIFF MUST DIE!

Pop favourite Cliff Richards has been sentenced to death by members of a cult religious group who have branded the baby faced star an EVIL puppet of SATAN.

"Cliff Richards must die", says Blackburn based Derek Qualcast, self proclaimed High Priest at the Church of the Latter Day Scientific Christologists of the Seventh Holy Grail. And he accuses Richards of using his music to preach evil to unsuspecting record buyers and fans.

"Richards is the antichrist", blasted Mr Qualcast, who is 57. "He is in league with the forces of darkness, and is sent by the Devil to lure us from the path of righteousness. The words of his songs are thinly veiled catalogues of sexual corruption. He preaches fleshy pursuits and sinful activities, such as girl on girl, topless relief, oral and shaving pleasures".

PORNOGRAPHIC

Mr Qualcast claims that Richards' hits contain Satanic messages. "Records such as 'Devil Woman' speak for themselves, while 'Carrie' clearly takes its name from the devil worship pornographic film of the same name. And 'Goodbye Sam, Hello Samantha' is an open invitation to young people to indulge in acts of unfathomable evil, possibly involving farmyard animals".

VIRGINS

Qualcast fears that Richards has already claimed the lives of thousands of young virgins, and goats. For he believes the secret of the baby faced star's boyish good looks is the blood of freshly killed victims, which he drinks every day. And worse still, he is convinced that 68 year old Richards practices voodoo, black magic and has the ability to turn himself into a bat.

Muslim style 'Fatwa' on Peter Pan of Pop

Richards – 'sent by Devil'

In a 15 year campaign to silence the singer Qualcast has visited every record shop in Blackburn, and one in Rochdale, sprinkling holy water on their doorsteps. But despite his efforts the ageless star's string of chart hits has continued uninterrupted. However, Mr Qualcast vows to continue the fight.

SPUNK

"It is a clear cut case of Good against evil," he told us yesterday. "The Bible tells us that on the seventh day it was written that the heavens shall open and he will be tempted three times for forty days and forty nights, and yea on the forth time the clouds shall part and down will rain the Devil's spunk and spawn and a multitude of frogs and boils, and so you shall know him by the name of Lucifer, and his name shall be Ahab, who begat Cain and Abel who begat George who begat Harry Webb who is called Cliff Richards. For so it is written, and so shall be", Mr Qualcast added.

EATING SMARTIES MADE ME GROW WOMEN'S TITS
~claims man

A Cleveland man yesterday claimed that Smarties made him grow women's tits.

Unemployed panel beater Bill Strimmer of Billingham claims that eating the candy coated chocolate sweets resulted in him developing a pair of 38 inch 'D' cup women's breasts.

"I was horrified, and embarrassed", Bill told us. "They were huge, with nipples and everything. I didn't know where to turn".

WOMEN'S

Despite support from his wife, who lent him a bra, Bill faced ridicule from workmates at the garage where he was employed, and eventually he was forced to quit his £10,000 a year job.

"I lost my job for having women's tits, and its all because of Smarties", says Bill, 42, who is claiming £2 million compensation from Smarties manufacturer Rowntrees for loss of earnings due to women's tits.

"I always ate Smarties, ever since I was a kid", he told us yesterday. "But the problems began when they introduced the blue ones." Within three days of eating the new blue coloured sweets, Bill noticed he was growing a pair of women's tits.

"I went to my doctor and he immediately asked if I'd been eating blue Smarties. He told me to stop, and sure enough the tits disappeared. But by then it was too late. I was already out of a job, and I was the laughing stock of the whole town."

TITS

A spokesman for Rowntrees confirmed that blue Smarties had been introduced for a limited period, but was able to state categorically that they did not cause women's tits.

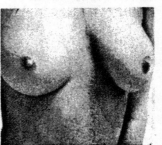

A pair of tits similar to the ones claimed to have been grown by Mr Strimmer

Mr Strimmer refused to make any comment until he had spoken to his solicitor. "The blue ones definitely made me grow women's tits and I'll sue them for every penny they've got", he told us yesterday.

Mr Strimmer last hit the headlines in 1972 when he claimed that sucking Olde English flavour Spangles had caused him to grow women's tits.

THE EYE AT NIGHT!

An Aberdeen woman may be forced to sell her house – because she claims TV astrologer Patrick Moore has been using his telescope to observe heavenly bodies – through her bedroom window!

PEEPING

Glenda McBride, 58, says she has been forced to dress and undress with her curtains closed since peeping Patrick had a new extra powerful lens fitted to his telescope at his observatory in Selsey, Sussex.

Astrologer Moore yesterday

"He ought to keep his boggly eyes fixed firmly on the stars, and not on my tits", said Glenda yesterday.

FARMER PALMER

GET ORF MOY LAAAND.

AAAARGH!!

PAW! PAW! OL' UNCLE AMOS 'AVE CAUGHT 'IS AAARM IN YON THRESHIN' MACHINE!!

OH LOR'. OI 'OPES IT'S ALROYGHT.

THAANK GAWD FER THAAT. OI THINKS IT'LL STILL WORK.

ROIGHT AMOS. YOU'M BAIN'T BE NO GOOD TO OI NOOW YOU ONE-AARMED BAASTARD. GET ORF MOY LAAAND!

LATER...

JETHROW - WHOY AIN'T EE BURNT DOOWN MOY BAARN YET?

OOH...AAR... UM...

E.M.P.T.Y

OI AALREADY GOT THE CLAIM FOORM FAALLED IN.

GLUG GLUG

X

HALF AN HOUR LATER...

OI BE DEVESTADED. THAAR BE FIFTY GRAANDS WORTH OF 'AY AN' A BRAAAND NEW COMBOYNE AARVESTER IN THAAR.

IT BE THEY TOWNIES WHAT SET 'ER ORFF. OI DON' KNOW WHAT MOY COOWS'LL BE EADIN' THIS WINDER...

NEXT MORNING...

ROIGHT BOY. LETS GO 'N POWST THIS YURR CLAIM FOORM TO THE INSUURAANCE COM-ANY.

WHICH ROLLER SHAALL OI TAKES?

ERM...

LET'S GO IN THE GOLD 'UN PAW. THE ONE YOU'M GOT AAFTER THAT BRAANCH BLEW ORFF THE HEDGE LAAAST MAAARCH.

IN BORCHESTER...

GIT OOWT O' THE WOY! ZUM OF US 'AS BIN UP SIN' THE CRAAACK O' DAWRN DIPPIN' SHEEP. BLOODY TOWNIE...

OH DEAR.

AND..

TSK. TSK.

JETHRO!

BLAM! BLAM!

!?

YIP!

BONZO? BONZO? WHAT'S GOING ON? WHAT'S HAPPENED?

'IM WON' BE WORRYIN' NO MORE O' MOY SHEEP BOY.

LATER...

2 HOURS LATER...

2 HOURS LATER...

♪

ROIGHT JETHRO. YOU'M CAAN MOVE 'EM OONT NOOW.

ROIGHT PAW.

?!

2 HOURS LATER...

HRUMPH.

2 HOURS LATER... EXCUSE ME. BUT THESE COWS ARE CLEARLY WALKING ROUND IN A CIRCLE.

YOU'M TOWNIES SHOULDN'T MEDDLE IN THE WOYS OF THE CUNDRY. YOU OUGHT TER BE MORE PATIENT.

2 HOURS LATER...

ROIGHT. THAATS THE LAAST 'UN.

THANK GOODNESS FOR THAT.

ZORRY TER 'AAVE 'ELD EE UP ZURR. MOYND 'OW 'EE GOES NOOW.

PAT PAT

♪

SWERVE

WHAT THE..?

SCREECH!

TWO HOURS LATER... CAAAN'T EE MOYKE THIS YURR TRAACTOR GO NO SLOWER JETHRO?

OOH AAR. CAAN OI TURN ORN THE SHIT THROWER NOOW PAW?

JESUS!

105

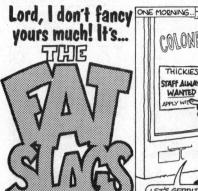

Lord, I don't fancy yours much! It's... THE FAT SLAGS

ONE MORNING...
HEY, LOOK!
COLONEL McBURGER
THICKIES! STAFF ALWAYS WANTED APPLY WIT
LET'S GERRUZ SELVES A JOB!

INSIDE...
HOY, WE'VE COME ABOUT THE JOBS IN THE WINDOW
RIGHT...WELL CAN YOU WRITE YOUR OWN NAMES, EH?
AYE!

WELL... YOU'RE A BIT OVERQUALIFIED, BUT WE'LL GIVE YOU A TRYOUT. YOU'LL FIND SOME UNIFORMS IN THE BACK ROOM...
...AND REMEMBER, THE MORE CUSTOMERS YOU SERVE, THE MORE YOU'LL BE PAID AT THE END OF THE WEEK!

'ERE THEY ARE, SAN
HEY, THEY LOOK ALRIGHT, DON'T THEY, EH?

SHORTLY...
C'MON, TRAY, HURRY UP...
ALRIGHT, ALRIGHT
...I'M FUCKIN' STARVIN'

R-R-RIP!
?
AW, FRIG! I'VE BUST 'EM

SAN, Y' CAN'T SEE ME TWAT, CAN YA?
ER... NAH!
COME ON

EEH, THEM CHIPS SMELL FUCKIN' LUSH

'ERE, TRAY, HERE'S US FIRST PUNTER...
AYE!

HELLO, GOOD MORNING AND WELCOME TO COLONEL McBURGERS! MY NAME IS TRACEY SANDRA
HOW MAY I BE OF ASSISTANCE TO YOU? HAVE A NICE DAY. PLEASE CALL AGAIN. THANK YOU!

ER... I THINK I'LL HAVE A BIG BURGER WITH FRIES, PLEASE
OI!

SHE'S MY PUNTER! I SAW HER FIRST, Y' FUCKIN' BITCH!
WELL, Y' SHOULD SHOUT LOUDER, Y' DAFT COW!!

WELL, I REALLY DON'T MIND WHO SERVES ME...
FUCK OFF, Y' CHEEKY GET! IT'S GOT NOWT T' DO WI' YOU. THIS IS BETWEEN ME AN' HER

WELL, REALLY!
THIS IS DISGRACEFUL. I THINK I'LL TAKE MY CUSTOM ELSEWHERE

YOU'D BE BETTER LAYIN' OFF CHIPS AN' BURGERS WI' AN ARSE LIKE YOURS ANYWAY
YEH! FAT ARSE!

NA-AA-AA-A-AA-AA-AA-

ERE, SAN!
IT'S TEN O'CLOCK! D' YA FANCY A BIT OF DINNER?

AYE! I'LL HAVE A COUPLE OF CHEESEBURGERS, A PARTY BUCKET OF CHIPS, A COUPLE OF HAMBURGERS, HALF A DOZEN BIG POUGHNUTS, ANOTHER HAMBURGER AN' A SMALL DIET COKE!
YOU ON A DIET, THEN!
AYE!

I RECKON I'VE GOT T' LOSE ABOUT FOUR POUNDS T' GET DOWN T' ME IDEAL WEIGHT
I'M LUCKY WI ME METABOLISM, ME. I CAN EAT LIKE A HORSE AN' I JUST BURN IT ALL OFF!
EEH, YOU LUCKY COW!

MICKEY'S MINIATURE GRANDPA

YOUNG MICKEY MARSTON'S GRANDFATHER WAS CONVINCED THAT A GYPSY'S CURSE HAD SHRUNK HIM TO A REMARKABLE FOUR INCHES IN HEIGHT...

BEING MIDGET-SIZED HAS ITS ADVANTAGES, MICKEY — YOU CAN CARRY ME AROUND EVERYWHERE IN YOUR POCKET!

YOUR KITE MAKES A SMASHING HANG-GLIDER, MICKEY — WHEEEEE!!

DON'T GRANDPA! YOU'LL BREAK IT! GRANDPA!

COME ON DAD, I THINK MICKEY WANTS TO PLAY BY HIMSELF FOR A WHILE

IT'S JUST THAT HE RUINS EVERYTHING MUM!

SEE YOU LATER MICKEY!

BUT SHORTLY..

HUH! THIS IS BORING! I'M OFF IN SEARCH OF ADVENTURE!

SCRAPBOOK 1943

IN THE PARK

PHEW! WHEN YOU'RE ONLY FOUR INCHES TALL, THIS LONG GRASS IS LIKE A JUNGLE!

WOW! THAT TOY BOAT IS JUST THE RIGHT SIZE FOR ME!

I BET THOSE KIDS WILL BE THRILLED TO HAVE A REAL-LIFE MIDGET AS CAPTAIN OF THEIR SHIP!

AND THIS SHARPENED MATCHSTICK IS AN IDEAL CUTLASS FOR A PINT-SIZED PIRATE!

SHIVER ME TIMBERS, KIDS! CAP'N GRANDPA'S THE NAME!

STAND BY TO LET ME BOARD THAT VESSEL, ME HEARTIES!

WHISPER WHISPER WHISPER

LOO-NEY, LOO-NEY, LOO-NEY...

OUCH! OOYAH! OW!

HA HA HA HA HA HA

BAH! SOMETIMES IT'S NO FUN BEING TINY!

HELLO! ONE OF THOSE KIDS MUST HAVE DROPPED THAT BOOK.

COR! THIS IS A SUPER STORY, ALL ABOUT WITCHES AND WIZARDS AND MAGIC SPELLS!

WINNIT THE WIZARD GOES FORTH

CRIPES! WHY DON'T I MAKE A SPELL TO NEUTRALIZE THE "SHRINKING CURSE" WHICH THAT GYPSY PUT ON ME?!

CHORTLE! I'LL BE BACK TO MY PROPER HEIGHT IN NO TIME!

BUT FIRST I'LL NEED SOME MAGIC INGREDIENTS. HMM, LET'S SEE ... "THE FEATHER OF AN EAGLE".....THE HORN OF A UNICORN"....

THAT'LL DO TO START WITH.

THE FEATHER IN THAT LADIES' HAT PROBABLY COMES FROM AN EAGLE, I SHOULD THINK.

HATS GALORE

AND I'VE GOT A FOOLPROOF PLAN HOW TO PINCH IT!

THANKS TO MY LILLIPUTIAN STATURE, I CAN DISGUISE MYSELF AS A MOUSE AND SCUTTLE INTO THE SHOP

DOUBTLESS THE WOMEN WILL ALL START SCREAMING AND JUMPING ONTO CHAIRS, AND IN THE CONFUSION I CAN ESCAPE WITH THE FEATHER!

EEK EEK EEK EEK EEK EEK EEEK

PLUCK!

BARGAINS

EEK EEK EEK EEK EEK EEK

HELLO? POLICE?

BARGA

ARF! A SPLENDID SUCCESS! NOW, WHAT'S THE NEXT INGREDIENT?

WINNIT THE WIZARD GOES FORTH

"THE HORN OF A UNICORN". HMM...

I'LL JUST LEAVE THIS LARGE ARTIFICIAL COW OUT HERE WHILE I HAVE A TEA BREAK.

JOE'S CAFF

DAIRY COUNCIL OFFICIAL

SNAP

GIVEN THE SCARCITY OF UNICORNS IN THIS AREA, I DARESAY THAT THE HORN OF A COW WILL DO JUST AS WELL.

HEY YOU! COME BACK HERE WITH THAT!

THAT'S THE MAN OFFICER — HE'S A CRACKPOT!

LAWKS! THEY'RE AFTER ME!

GASP, I MUST FIND SOMEWHERE TO CONCEAL MYSELF!

AHA! THAT LITTLE GIRL'S LUNCHBOX WILL MAKE THE PERFECT HIDING PLACE FOR MY MINISCULE BODY!

PARDON ME SIR, BUT I GOT THIS FEATHER TO HELP ME GROW BIG, AND NOW I'VE GOT THE HORN, AND I'M DESPERATE TO GET INTO YOUR DAUGHTER'S BOX.

...AND THE POST-VIOLENCE ENDING...

WELL, MRS MARSTON, HE TOOK QUITE A BEATING, BUT HE'LL PULL THROUGH ALL RIGHT.

Jack Black & his dog Silver in The Chocolate Cake Caper

Jack Black and his dog Silver were staying with his Aunt Meg at her vicarage home in the Cotswolds where Jack's Uncle Tom was the local vicar. One fine morning, he was out flying his kite.

GOSH, SILVER. ISN'T THIS FUN!

OH NO! MY KITE IS STUCK UP THE STEEPLE. WE'LL HAVE TO CLIMB UP AND GET IT

WOOF WOOF!

JACK! STOP! KEEP AWAY FROM THERE. THE STEEPLE IS IN A DANGEROUS CONDITION

OOYAH!

DO YOU SEE WHAT I MEAN? I'M AFRAID IT'LL COST OVER £100 TO REPAIR IT PROPERLY

GOSH!

IS THERE ANY WAY ME AND SILVER COULD HELP?

WHY, YES. WE'RE HAVING A FUND RAISING FETE IN THE CHURCH HALL TOMORROW. YOU COULD COME ALONG AND HELP IF YOU LIKE, JACK.

That evening....

WHAT ARE YOU DOING, AUNT MEG?

I'M BAKING A SPONGE CAKE, JACK. THERE'S A CAKE COMPETITION AT THE CHURCH FETE TOMORROW, WITH A TEN SHILLING PRIZE FOR THE BEST CAKE

GOSH. TEN SHILLINGS!

AND I'LL BE SELLING THESE ROCK CAKES FOR THE STEEPLE RESTORATION FUND

YUM YUM! THEY LOOK REALLY SUPER

The next day....

COME, ON SILVER, HURRY, OR WE'LL MISS THE JUDGING OF THE CAKE COMPETITION

CHURCH FETE TODAY

WOOF WOOF!

AND THE WINNER IS....

....MRS STEVENS' CHOCOLATE CAKE

CONGRATULATIONS MRS STEVENS. WHAT ARE YOU GOING TO DO WITH THE PRIZE MONEY?

WELL, I'M DONATING IT TO THE STEEPLE FUND AND I'LL BE SELLING SLICES OF THE CAKE TO RAISE MORE MONEY

THAT'S VERY KIND OF YOU MRS STEVENS

Shortly....

I'LL HAVE A SLICE PLEASE, MRS STEVENS. IT'S ALL IN A GOOD CAUSE

CHOCOLATE CAKE 6D

I'LL LET YOU HAVE TWO, JACK. ONE FOR YOU AND ONE FOR SILVER

But Jack didn't eat his slice....

HMM! THIS DOESN'T SEEM RIGHT

110

Secretly, Jack slipped away and ran two miles to the next village....

...and went to see his friend at the Cotswold Food Analysis Laboratory

AH, HERE WE ARE, SILVER

HELLO, YOUNG JACK. WHAT CAN I DO FOR YOU?

IT'S THIS PIECE OF CAKE, PROFESSOR JONES

IT MAY BE NOTHING, BUT I'D LIKE YOU TO TAKE A LOOK AT IT

The scientist got to work....

HMM.... I THINK YOUR SUSPICIONS ARE CONFIRMED

OH, DEAR!

THIS IS A SERIOUS BUSINESS....

....WE'D BETTER CALL THE POLICE AT ONCE

Back at the church....

IT'S ALL GONE, VICAR. I'VE RAISED TWO AND SIX ALL TOGETHER, PLUS THE TEN SHILLINGS PRIZE MONEY

CHOCOLATE CAKE 6D

WELL DONE, MRS STEVENS. EVERY LITTLE HELPS

Suddenly....

THAT'S HER!

MRS STEVENS, YOU'RE UNDER ARREST

SERGEANT BROWN, WHAT'S THIS ALL ABOUT?

IT'S ABOUT THAT CAKE UNCLE TOM

YOU SEE, MRS STEVENS TOLD EVERYONE IT WAS CHOCOLATE CAKE, BUT ACCORDING TO STRICT EEC REGULATIONS, A CHOCOLATE CAKE MUST CONTAIN AT LEAST 20% COCOA SOLIDS

INDEPENDENT TESTS SHOWED MRS STEVENS' CAKE CONTAINED ONLY 18%

WAIT A MINUTE. SO IN FACT IT WAS ONLY A 'CHOCOLATE FLAVOURED' CAKE!

THAT'S RIGHT! A CLEAR BREACH OF REGULATIONS

BUT.... BUT.... IT WAS MY MOTHER'S RECIPE

HERE YOU ARE MEG. MRS STEVENS IS DISQUALIFIED. THAT MAKES YOU THE WINNER

HOORAY FOR AUNT MEG!

WILL SHE GO TO PRISON, SERGEANT BROWN?

NO, SHE'S TOO OLD FOR THAT, JACK. BUT I'VE GOT ANOTHER IDEA....

Outside....

IT'S A GOOD JOB I OVERCOOKED MY ROCK CAKES. THEY'VE COME IN HANDY

TAKE THAT, YOU CHEATING BITCH

ME NEXT!

WOOF WOOF!

LETTERBOX

LetterBocks
Viz Commick
P.O. Box 1 PT
Newcasle upon Tyne,
NE99 1PT

*Do you have an interesting anecdote, opinion or a poem perhaps? Anything that our increasingly disillusioned readers may find vaguely amusing. If so, drop us a line at the address above. We'll be giving away a free pen for every letter we print in the next issue. But not necessarily to the people who wrote them.

Shut up you old bastards

PRIZE LETTER

I am sick and tired of old people complaining constantly about everything. They've had their fun in life, and now they're trying to spoil it for everyone else. I am 28 years of age.

T. Vulcan
Lancaster

I think that charming man Mr Kinnock should be the next Prime Minister.

Mrs P. Nimrod
Sterling

In response to my wife's letter (this issue), I can think of several good reasons why Mr Kinnock should *not* be Prime Minister. Firstly, he's Welsh. He's got freckles, he's nearly bald, and lastly, the little hair he has remaining is bright orange and styled like that of Mick Miller, the comedian.

Perhaps my wife would like to see this balding clown representing our interests at home and abroad? Frankly, I think not.

Mr P. Nimrod
Sterling

I am in the process of tracing my family tree and wonder whether any of your readers may be able to help me. My family comes originally from the Bolton area, and I believe my mother's name was Robson or Robinson. I believe I also have a sister who is older than me. Does anybody know them?

J. Sewell
Northampton

Following on from Mr Nimrod's letter (this issue), in the interests of political impartiality I think it only fair to point out that Mr Major, the Prime Minister, is ugly, boring and looks like a cross between Joe 90 and that lion bloke out of Beauty and the Beast.

Mr T. Tristar
Telford

Dog can look after itself

My dog may not be able to add up, spell my name or say "sausages" and "Esther" like the ones you see on 'That's Life', but he can hold his own in a fight with a badger.

J. Stealth
Darlington

I'm sure that if antique expert Arthur Negus were to visit my home he would turn his nose up at most of my furniture. Still, he's dead and I'm alive, so who's laughing now?

T. Gloster-Meteor
Durham

Kylie Minogue is my favourite pop star, and actress, so I wrote this poem for her.

Kylie, Kylie, so sweet and smiley,
Let's sing a song
In a 'rub-a-dub' styley.

Kylie, Kylie, so cute and twee,
Oh please Michael Hutchence
Give her one from me.

Lee Green
Lewisham

I don't see why dog owners should be fined if their dog fouls the pavement. If a dog owner was caught drink/driving, they wouldn't expect his dog to pay the fine.

This is clearly a case of double standards.

Mrs D. Kent
Wimbledon

Fancy a shag?

They say that all men are the same with the light off. Then perhaps some of your female readers would like to pop round for a shag? My electricity was cut off last week.

Richard Button-Mushroom
Ripon

Every once in a while my wife and I enjoy a romantic, candle-lit dinner and a smooch to our favourite record, before stripping off for a game of 'wheelbarrow'.

I wonder whether any other readers have quaint phrases which aptly describe their style of lovemaking.

M. Herringbone
Henley

I began drinking at the age of 16, and have been a heavy drinker now for over 20 years, spending a small fortune each week on beer, lager and spirits. But come 'Comic Relief' day I'm the one who's laughing, as I never have to waste money buying a stupid red nose.

I already have one!

I. P. Head
Middlesbrough

I don't see the point in speed limits and alcohol restrictions for motorists. I'm sure a lot of drivers get a thrill out of deliberately breaking these laws. I believe there should be no speed limit, and drinking should be allowed. I'm sure that once the novelty of driving at high speeds and whilst drunk has worn off, motorists will, of their own accord, begin to drive more slowly, sensibly and sober.

Mr I. Quinn
Dartford

Vegetarians tell us that it's wrong to kill defenceless animals. Several years ago my grandfather was bitten by a sheep. So animals are hardly defenceless, are they?

M. Blugeon
Worcester

WOULD YOU LIKE SOME MORE CAKE?

NO THANKS. I'M STUFFED.

Top Tips

MASHED potato looks a bit like snow, and is harmless for children.

H. Civic
Southampton

GIVE friends the impression that you wear contact lenses by blinking frequently and pulling down your lower eyelid.

Michael Hudson
Bingley

AVOID being mugged in the street by walking along behind a policeman and moving your lips and gesturing as if you are having a friendly conversation with him. If he turns round, simply look confused and ask him for directions to a nearby street.

R. Hollins
Hammersmith

WHEN travelling by train, jot down a note of any refreshments you require and pin it to your lapel. This will save you having to talk to the miserable bastard who is invariably serving in the buffet car.

P. Donnelly
Portsmouth

WEIGHT watchers. Weigh yourself each week. The difference between successive weights is the amount that you have either gained or lost.

A J Marsh
Tongham; Surrey

CONVINCE neighbours that you have an expensive car alarm by locking up your car and making loud, high-pitched whooping noises whilst walking away.

S. Black
Burnley

OBTAIN the effect of having a bald, yellow scalp by removing the skin from a bowl of custard which has set, and placing it on your crown.

I. Vandyke
Lancashire

KEEP your insurance company on their toes by ringing them to say that your roof has just blown off in a storm, then calling them back ten minutes later to say that you were mistaken.

I. Battenburg
Walsall

ATTACH a tag with your name and address on it to your house keys so that if they are lost, whoever finds them can return them to you. If there's room, mention the times that your house is empty so that they'll be sure to catch you in when they call.

P. Pegley
Hammersmith

STICK silk flowers to an old woolly hat to make it pretty for that special occasion

G. Richardson (Mrs)
Oxford

CUT your man's hair round a mousse ring mould instead of a pudding bowl if he is balding at the crown.

Mrs C. Sidiros
Greenford

How about Sir Cliff?

Isn't it about time Cliff Richard was honoured with the Knighthood he so richly deserves. After all, he's never taken drugs or had sex like many other so-called 'pop' stars. In fact, now that Princess Ann is getting divorced, wouldn't it be nice if he could marry her and become the King of England.

Mrs Martha Hienkel
Weighbridge

Three cheers for the Princess of Wales, with her cheeky smile, her beautiful frocks and those trend-setting hats. Well worth four million quid a year, I must say.

E. Tornado
Bedford

SIXTIES STARS SLAM SADDAM

Many of Britain's top groups from the sixties are up in arms about Iraq's invasion of Kuwait.

Indeed, several sixties hit-makers are believed to have been disappointed by the news that the war was over. "Some of them had been looking forward to getting out there and giving Saddam what for", a showbiz insider told us yesterday.

STORM

Saddam's invasion of Kuwait triggered a storm of protest from sixties chart toppers, among them Allan Clark, veteran frontman with The Hollies. "It was certainly an unjustified act of aggression", Clark fumed yesterday.

SORRY

Peter Noone, mop topped singer with Herman's Hermits, felt equally strongly. "You have to feel sorry for the people of Kuwait, and everyone else who has suffered in the conflict", blasted Noone, whose hits included "No Milk Today".

A sixties group.

"It's a shame about all the pollution that's been caused," he told us.

OPEN ALL HOURS

Gerry Marsden of Merseybeat sensations Gerry and the Pacemakers wasn't mincing his words either. He agreed with the 12 point UN resolutions against Iraq, and the principal that aggression should not pay. "I suppose you could say that", he told us yesterday.

Dave Clark, one time hitmaker with The Dave Clark Five, was yesterday unavailable for comment.

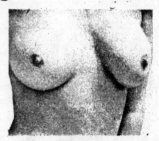
113

THE FLYING SCHOOL

BOSWELL ROAD JUNIOR SCHOOL WAS THE MOST UNUSUAL BUILDING YOU HAD EVER SEEN — IT WAS A GIANT ELECTRONIC FLYING WOODLOUSE, WHICH HAD BEEN BUILT BY THE HEADMASTER, MR SIMMONS, A BRILLIANT INVENTOR...

ONE MORNING

HURRY UP CHILDREN, IT'S NINE O'CLOCK — TIME FOR SCHOOL!

GOSH! I WONDER WHERE THE WOODLOUSE WILL FLY TO TODAY, MR SIMMONS!

WHO KNOWS, SUSIE? I ENTERED A RANDOM SET OF CO-ORDINATES INTO THE AUTO-PILOT, AND HAVE ABSOLUTELY NO IDEA WHERE WE WILL END UP!

INDEED, OUR JOURNEY COULD BE DANGEROUS. WE ARE EMBARKING UPON A FLIGHT INTO THE UNKNOWN, AS IT WERE.

BUT THAT'S ENOUGH CHIT-CHAT — LET'S GET ON WITH THE LESSON!

OPEN YOUR ARITHMETIC BOOKS AT PAGE TWELVE, PLEASE.

MAJESTICALLY, THE REMARKABLE CRUSTACEAN-LIKE FLYING SCHOOL ROSE INTO THE AIR...

TWO TWOS ARE FOUR, THREE TWOS ARE SIX, FOUR TWOS ARE EIGHT...

TWO HOURS LATER

.. AND THAT, CHILDREN, IS THE STORY OF HOW KING ROBERT THE BRUCE BURNED THE CAKES WHILST WATCHING A SPIDER...

SUDDENLY THERE WAS A TERRIFIC THUD, AND THE AIRBORNE SCHOOL CAME TO A SHUDDERING HALT

OH! WHAT'S HAPPENING?

WE'VE CRASHED INTO A TREE — BUT WHERE ON EARTH ARE WE?

THE HEADMASTER'S FACE WAS GRIM

CHILDREN, THIS IS SERIOUS. THE SHIP HAS CRASHED — AND THAT COULD POSSIBLY MEAN THAT IT IS DAMAGED BEYOND REPAIR!

WE ARE STRANDED HERE WITHOUT FOOD OR WATER —

DEATH BY STARVATION STARES US ALL IN THE FACE!

I AM SORRY, BUT WE HAVE NO ALTERNATIVE...

WE MUST EAT EACH OTHER IN ORDER TO SURVIVE!

SINCE I'M THE OLDEST, YOU CAN EAT ME FIRST.

SUSIE, GET THE BIG SAUCEPAN OUT OF THE SHIP. THE REST OF YOU COLLECT FIREWOOD, WHILST I SLIT MY THROAT.

BUT YOUNG 'BRAINBOX' SPENCER HAD ANOTHER IDEA...

SIR, WHY DON'T I WANDER UP THE LANE AND SEE IF I CAN FIND A SHOP SELLING PIES, OR PASTIES, OR SOMETHING?

JUST A PACKET OF CRISPS WILL DO ME, I'M NOT ALL THAT HUNGRY.

HMM. IT COULD BE WORTH A TRY.

AND I SUPPOSE I COULD CHECK HOW BADLY THE WOODLOUSE HAS BEEN DAMAGED, WHILE WE'RE WAITING FOR YOU TO RETURN.

AND SO —

GOOD LUCK BRAINBOX!

SHORTLY

WHAT LUCK! A DELICATESSAN! WITH ITS WIDE RANGE OF READY-TO-EAT FOODS, SUCH AS COLD MEAT, CHEESE ETC., IT'S AN IDEAL PLACE TO BUY PROVISIONS!

YE OLDE COUN... DELICATE...

HELLO! THOSE TWO MEN LOOK SUSPICIOUS!

THIS IS A STICK-UP! FILL THESE POLYSTYRENE TUBS WITH ALL YOUR POTATO SALAD, STUFFED OLIVES, HOUMOUS AND ROLLMOP HERRING — AND MAKE IT SNAPPY!

YEAH — AND DON'T HOLD BACK ON THE MUSHROOMS A LA GREQUE, OR IT'S CURTAINS FOR YOU!

FOOD ROBBERS! I MUST TELL THE HEADMASTER AT ONCE!

APART FROM A CRACKED SIDE LIGHT, THE SHIP WASN'T DAMAGED AT ALL!

MR SIMMONS! MR SIMMONS!

THE STARS WHO RE

In showbusiness, as in the sky at night, for every star that rises, so another must fade away. Famous names and favourite entertainers, for whom the show is over. Death, whether it be by accident, disease or natural causes, is no respecter of celebrity status. Eventually it catches up with us all.

But death does not always bring to a close the careers of the showbiz stars. For the entertainment world is littered with ghostly tales of stars who have simply refused to die.

KING'S RETURN TO THE THRONE

During his 46 years on Earth **ELVIS PRESLEY** never once visited Britain. But an unemployed plumber from Altringham claims to have come face to face with the King of Rock-'n'Roll in the lavatory of his council semi, 14 years **AFTER** the star's death.

Fifty-nine year old Bob Cartwright told us how he was awoken late one night by a groaning sound coming from his toilet. "I went to investigate, and couldn't believe what I saw", said Bob. "There, slumped across the lavatory seat, was Elvis Presley – the King of Rock'n'Roll. He was extremely overweight and had been eating a slice of pizza. He had got stuck and was obviously in some pain". Suddenly Elvis spoke.

ECHOED

"I'll never forget his voice. It seemed somehow distant, and echoed around the lavatory. But his Texas accent was unmistakable". Elvis asked Bob for a spoon which he needed to take some drugs. Bob rushed downstairs to the kitchen, but as he ran back upstairs towards the bathroom door he heard a loud flushing noise, and turned the corner only to see bubbling water disappear down the toilet.

U-BEND

As the bowl re-filled Bob heard the unmistakable sound of Elvis' voice coming from beyond the 'U' bend. "He was singing Suspicious Minds. I'll never forget sitting there with my ear in the bowl listening as his watery voice gradually faded away. It made the hair on the back of my neck stand on end, I can tell you".

HAMBURGER

Since that night, Bob believes that Elvis' ghost has returned to his house several times, on one occasion firing a gun at his television. "Fortunately, the ghostly bullet passed through the TV screen causing it no harm, but on another occasion Elvis caused a small fire in the kitchen when he left the grill on after cooking a hamburger late one night". Fortunately Bob was alerted by neighbours who spotted the flames and called the fire brigade.

Tree terror re~lived by dead idol

Diesel fitter Darren Peabody didn't believe in ghosts, until one night in 1986 he had an experience he will never forget. "I'd been to a friend's stag night at a local pub, and had been drinking heavily for several hours. It was pouring with rain and I couldn't find my car keys, so I was delighted when a stranger in the car park offered me a lift home in his mini. In the light of the full moon I made him out to be a young man, perhaps in his early thirties, with long dark curly hair, and make up.

HAIRPIN

"I began to tremble as the car sped along the narrow, winding road. Thunder and lightning flashed as the car careered around hairpin bends. I asked the driver to slow down, but it was too late, for at that very moment the car skidded out of control and hurtled towards a tree. I covered my face and braced myself for the impact.

URINE

The next thing I remember it was nine o'clock the next morning and I awoke to find myself lying in a pool of urine in the pub car park. There was vomit in my hair, and all over my clothes, and no sign of the young man in his mini. I made my way home and thought nothing more of the incident until a few weeks later when I mentioned what had happened to a friend. What he told me made my hair stand on end. For less than 120 miles from that very spot where the car span off the road, pop idol Marc Bolan had been killed in an almost identical accident exactly nine years earlier, almost to the month.

SOMERSAULTED

But the story doesn't end there. For six months later, after a night of heavy drinking, Darren drove past the same spot and spotted something moving behind the trees.

"Through the mist and fog I could just make out the silhouette of a white swan, with someone riding on it. Just like in the words of the T Rex song". Darren was so frightened that he lost control of his car, clipped a passing bus, and somersaulted into a ditch.

HOSPITAL

"The next morning I awoke in hospital. I explained to the police officers that I'd been frightened by the ghost of Marc Bolan but they simply would not believe me". Darren was fined £250 for driving with excess alcohol and banned from driving for 2 years.

CAMPBELL'S PEA SOUPER

Holidaymaker Stuart Ferguson got more excitement than he bargained for the day he and his family hired a rowing boat for a day out on Lake Windermere in the Lake District.

SNAPPED

Stuart, his wife Morag and their two children Angus, 2 and Crawford, 5 had been rowing for about an hour when their oar snapped. Stuart takes up the story.

"We were stuck in the middle of the lake with no land in sight. After a while it got dark, and a thick blanket of fog descended on the lake. It was eerie.

"Suddenly the ghostly calm was broken by a sound that made my hair stand on end. It was the roar of a bright blue rocket powered speed boat. The gleaming vessel emerged

SE TO DIE!

THIS IS YOUR AFTERLIFE

Since the death of Eamon Andrews, dressing room number 666 at Thames Television has stood empty. For not one single star in the world of showbusiness would dare use the room formerly occupied by the This Is Your Life presenter.

Andrew's successor Michael Aspel was the first man to enter the room after the Irishman's death. Seconds later he fled screaming, his grey hair standing on end. It was several moments before Aspel had calmed down enough to describe his terrifying experience to horrified TV executives. For inside the dark, dingy dressing room, he had come face to face with the headless ghost of his predecessor!

SPRANG

A Thames Television insider explained. "Eamon's ghost sprang out of the mirror and thrust a big red book at Michael. Fortunately Aspel fled, for the story goes that anyone who accepts the book from Andrews' ghost will immediately turn to stone".

Indeed one hapless cleaner, while dusting the light bulbs which surround the mirror in dressing room number 666, was accosted by the ghoulish figure, and took the book. She instantly turned to granite and her statue stands in the foyer of Thames TV as a warning to showbusiness celebrities and other would-be visitors to dressing room number 666.

Campbell's ghostly speedboat (above) emerges from the fog.

from the fog and pulled up alongside us. Without saying a word the driver threw us a rope.

FLAMES

"The next thing I knew we were being towed back to shore at speeds in excess of 600 miles an hour, and it wasn't long before we were safely back on dry land.

"As I walked up the pier, I turned to see the boat roar off at high speed, flip up into the air and explode in flames before sinking without trace.

"The next morning I returned to see if I could be of any help, but there was no sign of the mystery stranger or his boat. Not a single bit of wreckage had been washed ashore. I described the man to an old fisherman who was mending his nets at the nearby harbour, and asked if he knew him. "Yes", he said. "That was the ghost of Donald Campbell".

WHAT ARE GHOSTS?

There have been many attempts made to explain the phenomenon we loosely term 'ghosts'. Are they simple illusions created by our brains, or perhaps figments of our vivid imaginations. Or maybe its just our minds playing tricks on us. There have been many attempts made to explain this baffling phenomena.

AFTERLIFE

But what do the stars of showbusiness themselves think? Do the stars of stage and screen believe in the afterlife? And what is their idea of a ghost?

SUPERNATURAL

We asked three former TV Dr Who's to offer their explanations.

White haired former time lord **JON PERTWEE** has little time to ponder the mysteries of the supernatural. "I really haven't

given it a lot of thought", he told us yesterday. "But if you ring my agent next week he'll sort something our for you", he said.

Sauve time traveller **PETER DAVISON** is in no doubt about ghosts. "The human eye is like a camera, if you will", he told us.

RETINA

"Images are taken in and focused on the retina. When you see a ghost, it is merely the same process happening in reverse, the image being projected through your eyes and onto a wall, like a slide show, if you will".

CORNEA

"I don't know anything about ghosts, and frankly I don't particularly care", recent Doctor **SYLVESTER McCOY** told us. "And anyway, where did you get my number", he asked.

Garden haunted by green fingered ghoul

Police were baffled when they were called to the Blue Peter garden at the BBC Television Centre. Vandals had dug up plants, overturned a statue of the Blue Peter dog Petra, and poured bleach into the Italian sunken pond.

Detectives were baffled. The gate had been locked, and the garden is surrounded by a six foot wall. "It's as if the vandals simply walked in through a solid wall", he said.

BOX

That officer may have been closer to the truth than he realised, for paranormal experts now believe that Percy Thrower, the Blue Peter gardener and former TV bird impressionist, was responsible for the damage, and that his spirit had returned to Earth to haunt the garden.

"Percy often spoke of his wish to be buried in the Blue Peter garden, alongside the box for the year 2000", one former presenter told us. But that wish was never granted. Blue

Peter supremo Biddy Baxter refused to allow the burial, and even turned down an eleventh hour plea for Thrower's ashes to be scattered in the herbacious border.

"Percy Thrower's spirit cannot rest until his remains are taken to the Blue Peter garden", we were told. "And until they are, Thrower's ghost will haunt the garden, vandalising it once or twice every year".

Next week: The man who bought former Crackerjack funny man Peter Glaze's house reveals how the star's spectre has repeatedly foiled attempts to decorate the building by the use of a supernatural bungling comedy wallpapering routine.

MAXWELL STRAKER

I'M A TAPPIN', CLAPPIN', PEANUT PUSHIN', DOMINO TOPPLIN', COWPAT SLINGIN', MITTEN KNITTIN'...

RECORD BREAKER!

IN SEPTEMBER 1980, JAY GWALTNEY OF CHICAGO ATE AN 11 FOOT BIRCH TREE IN EIGHTY-NINE HOURS.

HMM. ELEVEN FOOT SIX. THAT'S JUST RIGHT!

CHOMP
GNN-NNN!

MMMF! JESUS!!

SO — BAH! THERE GOES MY POCKET MONEY FOR THE NEXT TWO YEARS.

DENTIST SALE! FALSE TEETH £100!

THE RECORD FOR TRAVELLING A PAIR OF 'UP' AND 'DOWN' ESCALATORS IS EIGHTY-FOUR HOURS, AND WAS SET BY NINE JOHANNESBURG FIREMEN IN 1987.

I'M GOING TO SMASH THAT RECORD HERE TODAY.

BIG SHOPPING CENTRE

DOO BE DOO BE DOOO-BA DOO BE

BISCUIT-U-LIKE

DOO BA DOO DA DOOO - DOO BA

BISCUIT-U-LIKE FLANNEL

BING BONG! LADIES AND GENTLEMEN- BIG SHOPPING CENTRE IS NOW CLOSING. WOULD ALL CUSTOMERS PLEASE LEAVE THE CONCOURSE BY THE NEAREST EXIT, AS WE WILL BE LETTING THE BIG DOGS OUT. PLEASE COME AGAIN. BING BONG!

BAH!

CHEESE

LATER— THE WORLD'S LARGEST COLLECTION OF CIGARETTE ROLLING PAPER BOOKLETS NUMBERS 2366 - AND IS OWNED BY PETER EMMENS OF SURREY.

NEWS'R'US Confectioners. Tobacconists. Newsagents.

WHAT A SAD INDIVIDUAL HE MUST BE.

NEVERTHELESS - I INTEND TO SHATTER THAT RECORD.

COULD I HAVE TWO THOUSAND THREE HUNDRED AND SIXTY SEVEN PACKETS OF RIZLAS PLEASE.

I'M SORRY MAXWELL. I CAN'T SELL THEM TO YOU. YOU'RE NOT SIXTEEN.

BUT THEY'RE FOR MY DAD, HONEST.

SORRY. YOU CAN'T HAVE THEM. MIND YOU - I'M GLAD YOU POPPED IN. YOU CAN TAKE YOUR DAD HIS NEWSPAPER.

HRUMPH!

The Times

THIS NEWSPAPER GIVES ME AN IDEA...

ROY DEAN OF KENT COMPLETED THE 'TIMES' CROSSWORD IN ONLY THREE MINUTES FORTY-FIVE SECONDS FOR HIS 1970 RECORD.

SO, AT HOME— GO! RIGHT. ONE ACROSS. UNDERWATER BANANA CRAWLS BACKWARDS TO TURKEY, WE HEAR. SIX, TWO, FOUR.

CLICK!

TWO HOURS LATER— ERM... HOLD ON. UNDERWATER BANANA CRAWLS BACKWARDS TO TURKEY, WE HEAR...

ZZZ-ZZZ...

...SIX, TWO, FOUR...

LATER— RICHARD NOBLE'S JET POWERED 'THRUST TWO' SET THE LAND SPEED RECORD AT 633.468 MPH BACK IN OCTOBER 1983.

DAD'S NEW CAR SHOULD BE ABLE TO BEAT THAT - AND SEE ME SAFELY INTO THE GUINNESS HALL OF FAME.

CRUMBS- I'M DOING FORTY ALREADY! I SHOULD EASILY BE TOUCHING SEVEN HUNDRED BY THE TIME I REACH THE HIGH STREET.

WOW! EIGHTY-FIVE!

THRUST

NINETY!! OH NO! LOOKOUT!

BIG TREE—

BANG!

LATER— DOOOOH! WHERE AM I?

YOU'RE IN HOSPITAL MAX, AND NORRIS McSQUIRTER IS HERE TO SEE YOU!

WHY? DID I BREAK THE LAND SPEED RECORD?

NO. AND ANYWAY - THAT WAS OVER EIGHTY YEARS AGO. YOU'VE JUST COME OUT OF THE WORLD'S LONGEST COMA!!

HEY! GREAT!

118

Will I See Her Again?

Steve Watson and his girlfriend Marion Harper were very happy. Their future looked rosy, but there was one cloud which loomed on the horizon.

OH MARION, I WISH I COULD SEE DISNEYLAND BEFORE I GO BLIND

I KNOW. BUT WE COULD NEVER AFFORD THE PLANE FARE, AND THE DOCTOR SAYS YOU'VE ONLY GOT A FEW DAYS CLEAR VISION LEFT

Then ...

HEY! LOOK AT THIS

STOCK CAR RACE TODAY

First Prize A TRIP TO DISNEYLAND

I WANT TO BORROW YOUR CAR, STEVE. CAN I HAVE THE KEYS?

DON'T BE A FOOL, MARION! YOU HAVEN'T EVEN PASSED YOUR TEST YET

DON'T WORRY. I'LL BE ALRIGHT

As Marion drove away ...

OH GOD! I HOPE SHE'S ALRIGHT. IF ANYTHING HAPPENS TO HER, I'LL NEVER FORGIVE MYSELF

Two hours later ...

DING DONG

AH! MARION'S BACK. SHE MUST HAVE FORGOTTEN HER HOUSE KEYS

But

STEVE WATSON?

YES ...

THERE'S BEEN AN ACCIDENT INVOLVING YOUR CAR

I'M AFRAID THE DRIVER WAS KILLED

MARION! OH, NO!

COULD YOU COME TO THE MORTUARY, SIR ...

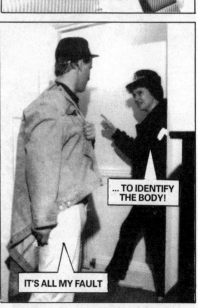

... TO IDENTIFY THE BODY!

IT'S ALL MY FAULT

CD.ST.GPD. Photos by Colin D. Colour by Deluxe.

The MODERN PARENTS

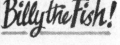

123

ROGER MELLIE

THE MAN ON THE TELLY

ONE DAY...

GREAT NEWS ROGER!

YEAH? DON'T TELL ME...

CHANNEL 4 HAVE ACCEPTED MY LATEST GAME SHOW IDEA - 'THE GOLDEN SHOWER'

IT'S JUST LIKE THE GOLDEN SHOT, BUT WITH PISS IN IT

NO ROGER. WE STILL HAVEN'T HEARD FROM THEM

WHAT IS IT THEN? NOT ANOTHER SUPERMARKET TO OPEN?

TELL 'EM TEN GRAND PLUS EXPENSES, OR THEY CAN PISS OFF AND GET KIETH CHEGWIN TO DO IT

NO ROGER, IT'S NOTHING LIKE THAT. THIS IS **REALLY** IMPORTANT! YOU'VE BEEN NOMINATED FOR AN AWARD...

TELEVISION PRESENTER OF THE YEAR!

YEAH!? FUCK ME! WHAT'S THE PRIZE?

THERE IS NO PRIZE ROGER

IT'S A PRESTIGE AWARD. IT WOULD BE A REMARKABLE ACHIEVEMENT TO WIN IT

YOU'D BE FOLLOWING IN THE FOOTSTEPS OF LAST YEAR'S WINNER MELVYN DRAG

OH YEAH. THAT ARTY PONCE WITH THE BUNGED UP NOSE

SINCE HE WON THE SOUTH WANK SHOW'S VIEWING FIGURES HAVE DOUBLED. OVER 50 PEOPLE WATCH IT NOW!

OKAY TOM. SO MARK MY CARD. WHO'S THE MR. FIX IT? AND ER... WHAT'S THE GOING RATE?

I BEG YOUR PARDON?

COME ON TOM. I WASN'T BORN YESTERDAY. WHOSE PALM DO I HAVE TO GREASE TO WIN THIS THING?

DON'T BE RIDICULOUS ROGER

THE AWARD IS JUDGED BY A PANEL OF HIGHLY REPUTABLE TELEVISION EXECUTIVES

BRIBERY IS ABSOLUTELY OUT OF THE QUESTION

YEAH YEAH YEAH... AND PIGS CAN FLY, I KNOW. COME ON TOM...

A GRAND? TWO GRAND? WHAT'S THE SCORE?

NO ROGER! IT'S ALL ABOVE BOARD. NO MONEY CHANGES HANDS

NO MONEY EH? SO WE'RE TALKING **NOSE CANDY** ARE WE? **SHOWBIZ SHERBET**. SNIFF SNIFF, SAY NO MORE!

LISTEN ROGER. PERHAPS IT WOULD BE BEST IF YOU JUST FORGET ABOUT THE AWARD

JUST TURN UP ON THE NIGHT, KEEP YOUR FINGERS CROSSED AND WHO KNOWS - YOU MAY WIN

THE AWARD CEREMONY IS QUITE AN OCCASION. THERE'S A 6 COURSE MEAL, COMPLIMENTARY DRINKS AND A ROYAL GUEST OF HONOUR

HEY! NOSH, FREE BOOZE, AND I GET TO MEET THE QUEEN EH!

WELL... NOT NECESSARILY THE QUEEN

HEY! I'LL BE THERE TOM! THAT'S MY KIND OF PARTY!!

A FEW DAYS LATER

VENOR HOTEL

TONIGHT T.V. PRESENTER OF THE YEAR AWARDS

GOOD EVENING SIR MARMALADE. CONGRATULATIONS ON YOUR APPOINTMENT AS HEAD OF THE BBC

ROGER AND I ARE WORKING ON A FEW PROJECTS THAT MAY BE OF INTEREST TO YOU

HE SHOULD BE HERE BY NOW. HE'S BEEN NOMINATED FOR AN AWARD YOU KNOW

REALLY?

HI TOM. SORRY I'M LATE. IT'S THIS AWARD. I'M JUST **SO** NERVOUS!

AH ROGER. I'D LIKE YOU TO MEET...

MY STOMACH'S BEEN GIVING ME HELL. I'VE BEEN PISSING RUSTY WATER OUT ME ARSE ALL AFTERNOON!

WELL, REALLY!

RIGHT. WHERE'S THE BAR? I'M FUCKING PARCHED!

COME ON ROGER. THERE'S A LOT OF IMPORTANT PEOPLE I'D LIKE YOU TO MEET

HEY! JUST THE TICKET! I'LL HAVE A COUPLE OF THESE FOR STARTERS!

HEY LOOK TOM! IT'S HER WITH THE TEETH. ESTHER WHATSIT OFF 'THAT'S LIFE'

HERE. WATCH THIS!

HEY! ESTHER! I'VE GOT SOMETHING FOR YOUR SHOW

LOOK AT THAT! JUST LIKE A POTATO EH?

IT'S EVEN GOT A BIT OF CHEESE ON IT!

124

Victorian Dad